Messenger, Lisa. Collective Hub. 365 Days of Wellness.

ISBN: 978-0-6450340-0-4
First published in 2021 by The Messenger Group Pty Ltd
Project Management: Emily Karamihas
Editing: Lucy E. Cousins
Sub-editing: Emily Ditchburn & Claire Hey
Creative Direction, design & illustration: Emily Karamihas
Photographic inspiration for illustration: Arielle Vey

Distribution Enquiries: lisam@collectivehub.com
Media Enquiries: teagan@collectivehub.com
PA & Administration Enquiries: teigan@collectivehub.com

This is proudly a Collective Hub & Lisa Messenger product,
lisamessenger.com collectivehub.com

365 days of wellness

COLLECTIVE HUB
journal

intro

2020 was tough. We experienced a lot – as individuals and as
a unified world. Bushfires, a global pandemic, climate crisis,
economic instability and racial vilification. Not to mention our
own personal experiences. People were discombobulated.

Confused. Lost. Missing a sense of purpose.

Sometimes our rituals and routines went by the wayside. We
ate too much. Drank too much. Stifled our fears and feelings.
I, too, was guilty at times for many of these. I made excuses.
I let my practices slide – even though I know (and knew) in
my heart what was good for me.

As I travelled through the latter half of 2020 I thought: let's
come into 2021 with a playbook on wellness that we can follow
along together, myself included, on a daily basis.

So we've set up an exclusive Facebook group (search and join
Collective Hub Club) where we can all unite. Where instead of
feeling alone in this, we can go through these things together –
strengthening connections.

I know, for sure, that when we do things together, when we gamify something, when we cheer one another on from the sidelines and when we have a shared goal and a shared sense of purpose, then anything is possible.

During 2020, many people reached out to me about how isolated they felt. How they didn't feel they had a sense of purpose. How they were worried about their health and wellbeing.

I witnessed my brother-in-law spend two weeks in isolation in a closed hotel room with no fresh air after my father-in-law passed away. The whole time I wondered why the powers that be couldn't have set up some kind of intraweb for guests in a similar position, to share their experiences and support one another.

I will commit to doing the activities most days with you so that we truly are all doing something in unison together.

Let's go!

Lisa xo

how to

Welcome to a year of wellness challenges!

This book is designed for you to follow along on each challenge, or to deep dive into the challenges that speak directly to you and your way of living. Each day has an activity for you to get stuck into (as well as some of my musings and relevant resources) and some space for you to write down your thoughts and feelings.

Now, this book is a little different in that we're going to follow along with you in real time in a closed Facebook group called Collective Hub Club (request to join). We'll have special guests and yours truly jumping in each of the 365 days and doing the exercises outlined in this journal in real-time with you. I really hope you share your wellness journey with us in there as well. This is the ultimate print and digi mash-up experience!

I'm hoping that this book will challenge, inspire and encourage you to carve out some time for the most important person in your world. And that's YOU.

contents

january

SPARK CREATIVITY

Want to start the year with motivation, inspiration and a swag of ideas? The answer is creativity!

Even if you don't consider yourself a creative person, you can still benefit from tapping into that side of your brain. In fact, studies show that practising creativity can encourage feelings of happiness, improve brain function and boost your immune system, and it could even make you smarter (seriously).

So, this month is dedicated to finding creativity and playfulness in our everyday lives. We want you to try new things, improve your skills, and get involved with activities you might find challenging or out of the box. You never know, you might just find a new hobby, career or friend by the end of it!

It's time to use that brain of yours in new and different ways, and to find out what secret talents you have hidden away.

WRITE DOWN SIX WAYS YOU THINK YOU ARE CREATIVE AND STICK THE PAPER TO A MIRROR YOU LOOK AT EVERY DAY. READ THEM AND FINISH BY SAYING "I AM CREATIVE". MINDSET IS EVERYTHING.

1. _____

2. _____

3. _____

4. _____

5. _____

6. _____

Lisa's Musing

Remember we are all creative in different ways. What works for me won't necessarily work for you. The trick is to keep trying things. Keep believing. FYI, here are a few ways I think I'm creative to give you some jump points: vision boarding, interior decorating, coming up with ideas for books and new products, coming up with spontaneous outings and surprises, playing with different mixes of ingredients when cooking.

Read: *Thinking Fast and Slow* by Daniel Kahneman

ENJOY BLUE-SKY THINKING. TAKE TIME TODAY TO LIST THINGS YOU'D DO IF MONEY AND CIRCUMSTANCE WEREN'T AN ISSUE. WHAT WOULD YOU DO? HOW WOULD YOUR LIFE LOOK? MANY SUCCESSFUL PEOPLE USE THIS TECHNIQUE TO HELP THEM THINK WITHOUT LIMITS.

- _____
- _____
- _____
- _____
- _____
- _____
- _____

Lisa's Musing

You will be surprised by the simplicity of this exercise and the outcomes it can bring. When you're doing it, get quiet, let go of all limiting beliefs and let your thoughts flow. I revisit this exercise every six months. I am blown away by how much has come to fruition. The art of dreaming out loud and writing it down has immense power.

"Everyone is a genius. But if you judge a fish by its ability to climb a tree, it will live its whole life believing that it is stupid."

– Albert Einstein

START THE DAY BY GRABBING YOUR COFFEE, CHAI, TEA OR SMOOTHIE, SITTING SOMEWHERE COMFORTABLE AND DOODLING IN THIS SPACE. LET YOUR MIND RUN FREE AND DRAW WITHOUT AGENDA. USING YOUR BRAIN IN THIS WAY CAN HELP YOU CARVE OUT ROOM IN YOUR MIND TO SOLVE PROBLEMS, BRAINSTORM AND BE CREATIVE.

Lisa's Musing

Do not let yourself feel overwhelmed by this. I am a terrible drawer. But when I remove that limiting belief and just doodle, write, scrawl, it is quite amazing what comes out of my head. Let yourself be free. You might surprise yourself.

There are lots of local classes, but a good place we love for online drawing lessons is **theartstudiony.com.**

EVERYONE IS CREATIVE TO SOME DEGREE, BUT SOME FOCUS MORE ON THEIR SKILLS THAN OTHERS. TODAY, WRITE A LIST OF THE THINGS YOU DID AS A CHILD THAT WERE CREATIVE. THESE COULD BE THE GAMES YOU PLAYED, YOUR DRESS UP-BOX, THE WAY YOU CREATED CASTLES IN THE SAND. REMIND YOURSELF OF HOW YOUR CREATIVE MIND WORKED WHEN IT DIDN'T HAVE PRESSURE, RESPONSIBILITY AND EXPECTATION ON IT.

- _____   - _____
- _____   - _____
- _____   - _____
- _____   - _____

Liza's Musing

Yesterday I was looking after my four-year-old niece. In one afternoon, we dressed up as Elsa and Anna and sang *Let It Go*. We went to Flower Power and bought 16 veggies to plan out a new garden. We made up a play about a small policeman that lived on our shoulders, and we plaited our hair. Would I have done this with my best friend? Probably not. Did I feel uninhibited and un-judged doing it with my niece? Absolutely! Today I'll do something just as fun with a friend my own age. Just you watch.

"Go back. Way back to that little innocent girl walking around barefoot on the sidewalk in the summer sun. Worry less. Be like her."
– Anonymous

JANUARY 5

TAKE 15 MINUTES TODAY TO STARE AT THE CLOUDS AND SEE HOW MANY SHAPES YOU CAN IDENTIFY. NOT ONLY IS THIS WORKING YOUR CREATIVE MIND, BUT IT ALSO HAS THE SAME BENEFITS AS MEDITATION. MAKE SURE YOU TAKE LONG, CONSIDERED BREATHS. WRITE OR DRAW WHAT YOU SEE IN THE CLOUDS BELOW!

Lisa's Musing

Sounds simple. Will have a profound effect. Stillness. Gratitude.

"Creativity is inventing, experimenting, growing, taking risks, breaking rules, making mistakes, and having fun."
– Mary Lou Cook

**TAKE A MOMENT TO REMEMBER WHO YOU WERE BEFORE
'ADULT RESPONSIBILITIES' OF LIFE CAME DOWN ON YOU.
WHAT MAKES YOU SMILE, LAUGH, DREAM?**

Write down 10 hobbies you wish you had more time for. Then write down two hobbies you are now going to make time for.

1. _____   6. _____

2. _____   7. _____

3. _____   8. _____

4. _____   9. _____

5. _____   10. _____

1. _____   2. _____

Lisa's Musing

In the day-to-day we often forget what makes us come alive. What are some activities that make you feel happy? Some of mine are rock climbing, surfing, galloping on horses and doing a great spin class.

Get out of your comfort zone and try something new!
Try your local TAFE for short courses or **udemy.com**.

GO FOR A WALK TODAY WITHOUT MUSIC OR PODCASTS, AND TURN YOUR PHONE TO SILENT. LOOK AROUND FOR MOMENTS OF CREATIVITY. ARE THERE BEAUTIFUL FLOWERS, COLOURFUL GRAFFITI, FUN WINDOW DISPLAYS TO TAKE INSPIRATION FROM? WHAT SOUNDS CAN YOU HEAR? TRY TO STOP THINKING (OR WORRYING!) ABOUT YOUR TO-DO LIST SO YOUR MIND CAN GET A BREAK.

Write down or draw what you saw, heard or smelled.

lisa's musing

I'm so excited for what you discover today. I can't wait for you to share it with me and I'll be doing the same. This is an electric little exercise that I'm sure will make you come alive in ways you never imagined. Tag me **@lisamessenger** to share your experience!

"In nature nothing is perfect. And everything is perfect."
– Alice Walker

START AN 'IDEAS JOURNAL' THAT TRAVELS WITH YOU, AND FILL IT WITH FIVE IDEAS TODAY THAT YOU ARE EXCITED ABOUT. MAKE SURE YOU ADD THE CRAZY IDEAS, THE OBVIOUS IDEAS, THE IDEAS THAT WERE INSPIRED BY SOMEONE ELSE. THERE IS NO JUDGEMENT IN YOUR IDEAS BOOK, IT'S JUST FOR YOU.

Use this page to write down five impossible ideas. Don't worry how unrealistic they are, the point is to dream big.

1. _____

2. _____

3. _____

4. _____

5. _____

Okay, so blatant plug here – did you see we recently started doing blank notepads over at collectivehub.com? Small tip: I love creating the products that I love to use every day.

"To practice any art, no matter how well or badly, is a way to make your soul grow. So do it." – Kurt Vonnegut

JANUARY 9

VISIT A BOOKSTORE OR A LIBRARY AND SEEK OUT THE SECTIONS THAT INSPIRE YOU THE MOST. ARE THERE ANY TITLES OR BOOKS THAT SPARK YOUR IDEAS? WRITE DOWN THE NAMES OF THE BOOKS BELOW AND COMMIT TO READING THEM OVER THE NEXT YEAR.

- _____
- _____
- _____
- _____
- _____
- _____
- _____

I get so much of my inspiration from sitting in bookstores. I love new and second-hand bookstores and could (and do!) spend hours upon hours in them. Just looking at titles and flicking through pages will give you jump points for pretty much any new project.

Some of my fave bookstores in the world are Gertrude & Alice in Bondi, Sydney (**@gertrudeandalice**), and Tsutaya Books in Daikanyama, Tokyo (**@daikanyama.tsutaya**). Even if you can't get there in person, you can follow them virtually.

REARRANGE A ROOM IN YOUR HOME. MOVE THE FURNITURE TO A NEW CONFIGURATION, OR MAKE A READING NOOK OR A CREATIVE CORNER. EVEN JUST CHANGING A SMALL PART OF YOUR HOME CAN HELP SPARK CREATIVITY AND GIVE YOU A FRESH PERSPECTIVE.

Use this space to write down the areas of your home that you'd like to declutter. This will come in handy in a future challenge!

Lisa's Musing

My mother-in-law does this weekly, if not daily. She rarely buys new furniture but she is a creative wizard when it comes to freshening up the house. She says (and I agree) that it keeps everything feeling fresh and new and sparks little bits of creativity every time she does it. Best part? It's free!

Follow **@threebirdsrenovations** and **@crystalbailey** for great interior inspiration. Pinterest is also a favourite of mine!

JANUARY 11

CLOSE THE BLINDS, PUT SOME ESSENTIAL OILS IN A DIFFUSER AND TAKE 15-20 MINUTES TO CLEAR YOUR MIND. THE SIMPLE ACT OF GIVING YOUR MIND PERMISSION TO WANDER FREE WILL HELP RELEASE THOUGHTS AND IDEAS THAT YOU MIGHT NOT HAVE LISTENED TO DURING YOUR BUSY DAY.

Use this space to write down any thoughts that come to you.

Lisa's Musing

I am big into my essential oils. As well as popping them in a diffuser, I'll often splash a bit around in the shower, pop some on my pillow and rub them on to my temples, wrists and belly.

Try diffusers from dōTERRA and Husk. And some of my fave essential oils are by Perfect Potion and Enfleurage.

SPEND SOME TIME PEOPLE WATCHING TODAY. AS YOU OBSERVE THEM, MAKE UP THEIR LIFE STORY BASED ON WHAT YOU SEE. BEING ABLE TO CREATE LIVES FOR OTHER PEOPLE USES IMAGINATION AND CREATIVITY. TAKE TIME NOW TO CONSIDER THESE QUESTIONS ABOUT YOURSELF WITH THE SAME CREATIVITY.

What was your first thought when you woke up this morning?

When was your first disappointment?

What makes you happy?

Lisa's Musing

It's no secret I am perpetually fascinated by human nature and psychology. One of the reasons I started my print magazine was because my curiosity got the better of me. I wanted to know the story behind the story. What made people who they were? Why they did what they did? It is so much fun, so interesting, and one of my most indulgent creative pursuits. Everyone has a story to tell, and we can learn something from everyone. When you start exploring like this, it opens up all sorts of possibilities and thoughts for our own lives.

Read *Talking to Strangers – What we Should Know About the People we Don't Know* by Malcolm Gladwell.

JANUARY 13

**CHOOSE A BOOK TO READ THAT IS OUT OF YOUR COMFORT ZONE...
SOMETHING YOU WOULD NEVER NORMALLY PICK UP. MAKE A CONSCIOUS
EFFORT TO LOOK FOR THE VALUABLE LESSONS IN IT.**

Write down three things you learned from this book below:

Lisa's Musing

Be unafraid to be purposefully counterintuitive. It's such a fun
exercise to push yourself and get just a little uncomfortable. Who
knows, you may love what you find. Or, at the very least, you won't,
and you won't go there again. You have nothing to lose!

Go into your local bookstore and look for 'staff picks' or
Google a category that is totally off your normal radar.

DO A PHOTO SHOOT THAT CAPTURES PART OF YOUR DAY. LOOKING THROUGH A LENS CAN HELP YOU SEE THE ORDINARY IN A NEW AND EXCITING LIGHT. WHERE CAN YOU SEE BEAUTY THAT YOU WOULDN'T HAVE SEEN OTHERWISE?

How was it different seeing your life through the lens?
Did you discover anything you hadn't noticed before?

Lisa's Musing

Like many of us, I have a love-hate relationship with social media. The love part is that I get to constantly look for inspiration to share. It helps me to see things in a different way. And I am able to connect with so many beautiful people in our community. But today, instead of doing it for everyone else, do it for yourself.

Check out these Instagram accounts for inspiration:
@adamsenatori, @brahmino, @ilhan1077.

**BUY SOME INDIVIDUAL FLOWERS AND LEAVES AND ARRANGE
THEM IN YOUR OWN WAY, THEN DISPLAY THEM IN YOUR HOME.
BE CREATIVE WITH COLOURS, TEXTURES AND SHAPES.**

Draw your arrangement below or paste in a photo. Share it with us
#collectivehub or post it in our Facebook group: Collective Hub Club.

Lisa's musing

A friend of mine's partner sadly passed away recently. People sent
flowers upon flowers. By day three she'd had enough – it was a
constant reminder of what had happened. So, I had a thought.
I dismantled the bunches and put every flower out on a long table.
We then sat and made new creations that were exactly what she
wanted. It gave us a cathartic and creative outlet and we repurposed
well-meant gifts into something with personal meaning.

A quick "how to arrange flowers" search on YouTube will give
you all sorts of great ideas. Or just be brave and freestyle!

JANUARY 16

WRITE A LETTER TO YOUR FUTURE SELF, SEAL IT AND PUT A DATE ON THE FRONT FOR ONLY YOU TO OPEN. DON'T TALK ABOUT WHAT YOU HOPE HAS HAPPENED, INSTEAD TALK TO YOUR FUTURE SELF AS YOU WOULD A FRIEND AND TELL THEM ABOUT THE THINGS THAT MAKE YOU HAPPY RIGHT NOW, AND WHAT YOU CURRENTLY LOVE ABOUT YOUR LIFE.

Paste your letter here.

I did this in 2004 when I completed a course called the Hoffman Process, which was completely life-changing for me. I didn't open it until 2014 – a decade later. It was truly remarkable what had come to light when I consciously chose to live a life I was courageous enough to commit to paper about 10 years earlier.

Check out **hoffmanprocess.com.au**.

TRY SOMETHING COMPLETELY DIFFERENT TODAY – IT COULD BE A NEW FOOD YOU'VE NEVER EATEN, A DIFFERENT FITNESS CLASS, OR PERHAPS IT'S GOING SOMEWHERE YOU'VE NEVER BEEN. STRETCH YOURSELF TO MOVE OR ACT IN A COMPLETELY DIFFERENT WAY.

Describe the last time you were out of your comfort zone.

_____

_____

_____

_____

_____

_____

Lisa's musing

Just doing something counterintuitive pushes and expands us in ways we never thought possible. Let's do this. We're all in it together today.

Check out **classpass.com.au** or **redballoon.com.au** for some ideas and thought starters.

**ASK FIVE FRIENDS FOR THEIR FAVOURITE SONG SO YOU CAN CREATE
A NEW PLAYLIST TO LISTEN TO IN THE CAR, ON THE BUS OR ON A WALK.
MUSIC IS GREAT FOR THE CREATIVE MIND, AND THESE NEW SONGS WILL
MAKE YOU THINK, LISTEN AND HEAR DIFFERENT IDEAS.**

Friend _____   Song _____

Friend _____   Song _____

Friend _____   Song _____

Friend _____   Song _____

Friend _____   Song _____

Lisa's musing

My sister and I do this all the time. We are both trying to be better
runners so we keep creating new playlists to inspire and push each
other. Remixed '90s is our go-to at the moment!

*"Music has healing power. It has the ability to take
people out of themselves for a few hours."* – Elton John

JANUARY 19

SUPPORT LOCAL ARTISTS BY VISITING A GALLERY, THE MARKETS, OR SEARCHING ONLINE. CONTACT SOME OF THEM AND TELL THEM YOU LOVE THEIR WORK, OR SHARE THEIR WORK ON YOUR SOCIAL MEDIA.

Add their names here so you can always reference them in the future.

_____

_____

_____

_____

_____

_____

Lisa's Musing

This is one of my all-time fave things to do. I love chatting to local artists, and also doing a bit of a shoutout on social media to share the love. Some of the greatest brands started at markets.

Etsy is a great place to start, as well as **buyfromthebush.com.au**.

ORGANISE A DINNER PARTY FOR YOURSELF OR YOUR FAMILY, CHOOSE A THEME AND DRESS THE TABLE ACCORDINGLY. SEE HOW MANY CREATIVE IDEAS YOU CAN COME UP WITH FOR DECORATIONS.

Write your favourite dinner menu ideas here.
What cocktails will you serve? What's for dessert?

_____

_____

_____

_____

_____

Lisa's Musing

My partner and I have a 'dinner for 16' every month. We meet so many creative people from so many industries, but often we can only spend an hour with them in a meeting. So we love bringing together random strangers once a month for a creative feast. With closer friends we often do a themed cook-off competition night – our latest was a pizza night where everyone had to bring one unusual ingredient.

We love Pinterest for dinner party ideas (and any kind of party, really!).

DRAW A MINI VISION BOARD ON THIS PAGE OF THINGS YOU WANT TO ACHIEVE THIS YEAR. DON'T WORRY ABOUT HOW GOOD THE DRAWINGS ARE, YOU JUST NEED TO CREATE AN IMAGE THAT WILL SPARK JOY IN YOU.

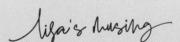

Lisa's Musing

If you scroll through my insta, you'll see a DIY video where I bought six $30 soundproof panels from Bunnings and covered an entire wall. In the same vid are $3 Besser blocks I used to create a side desk. You can get super creative on a shoestring. For me that's half the fun.

"Your current situation is giving you an opportunity to re-evaluate what you want." – Tashabee

DO 15 MINUTES OF MEDITATION TWICE TODAY, TO HELP SILENCE THE CHATTER IN YOUR MIND. NOTICE HOW IT MADE YOU FEEL AFTERWARDS AND HOW YOU SLEEP TONIGHT.

Use this page to write down anything that's on your mind that is making you stressed. Doing this before a meditation can help calm the mind.

Lisa's musing

Find a quiet corner and grab a cushion or a yoga mat.
For me, this creates the sense of a safe 'me' space.

Check out apps **Headspace**, **Calm** or **Insight Timer**.

FOLLOW 10 NEW CREATIVE PEOPLE ON SOCIAL MEDIA WHO INSPIRE YOU – THEY DON'T HAVE TO BE ARTISTS. CHOOSE PEOPLE WHO INCORPORATE CREATIVE THOUGHT INTO THEIR LIVES IN SOME WAY.

Write down five ideas from these accounts that you gravitated towards:

_____

_____

_____

_____

_____

_____

_____

Lisa's Musing

Don't know where to start? Just find one account you love. Then have a look at who they follow or interact with. But beware, it can become a never-ending rabbit hole, so set yourself a time limit.

~~~~~~~~

Some hashtags to follow are #localartist, #localartistsupport and the local art scene in your specific area, of course.

THINK ABOUT ALL THE CREATIVE THINGS YOU HAVE ACHIEVED THAT YOU'RE SUPER PROUD OF. LOOKING AT PAST ACCOMPLISHMENTS CAN SPARK YOUR INSPIRATION FOR FUTURE ONES.

List five of your biggest creative accomplishments here:

1. _____

2. _____

3. _____

4. _____

5. _____

Lisa's Musing

It's sometimes only in looking backwards that we are able to look forward. I love delving into my past achievements and feeling gratitude for them. It's not until you spend a few minutes thinking back that you really become aware of how much you've actually achieved. You might surprise yourself with just how far you've come.

"You can't use up creativity. The more you use, the more you have."
– Maya Angelou

ENJOY THE POWER OF PLAY AND SPEND TIME WITH ANIMALS, CHILDREN OR CREATIVELY MINDED PEOPLE TODAY. ENGAGING IN THE SIMPLE ACT OF PLAYING CAN STIMULATE YOUR MIND.

When was the last time you really laughed? Who were you with? Use the space below to write down your memories.

_____

_____

_____

_____

_____

_____

_____

Lisa's Musing

Sometimes I'll volunteer at local animal shelters or aged-care facilities, or offer to babysit for the afternoon. Whenever I do this I become totally present in the moment, and these times are some of my most enjoyable and magical memories.

"Creativity is intelligence having fun." – Albert Einstein

JANUARY 26

USE YOUR BRAIN A LITTLE DIFFERENTLY AND LEARN FIVE WORDS IN A NEW LANGUAGE TODAY. THINK OF IT AS PREPARATION FOR YOUR NEXT HOLIDAY. LEARNING ANOTHER LANGUAGE IS A WORKOUT FOR YOUR BRAIN AND CAN SPARK NEW IDEAS.

Write your words down here along with the translation
(and even how to say them if you like!).

1. _____

2. _____

3. _____

4. _____

5. _____

Lisa's Musing

Okay, I have to admit I am terrible at this. Maybe it's because I never studied languages at school so my brain just doesn't seem to pick up on them. Having said that, when I'm in situ (as in actually IN the country where the language is spoken) it's extraordinary how quickly I pick up a language. On my last trip to Italy my fiancé said I got up to around 90 words. The lesson – learn your way. If you follow what works for someone else you can often be left feeling like a bit of a dummy.

"Creativity is inventing, experimenting, growing, taking risks, breaking rules, making mistakes, and having fun." – Mary Lou Cook

JANUARY 27

COOKING IS AN ACHIEVABLE CREATIVE PURSUIT THAT IS GREAT FOR INSPIRATION, SO TONIGHT CHOOSE A NEW RECIPE AND COOK FROM SCRATCH. SHOW US YOUR CREATION #COLLECTIVEHUB

My earliest memories of cooking are:

When I cook I feel:

I wish I could cook:

Follow me on Instagram @**lisamessenger** - I've taken
to dropping some of my favourite recipes and doing little
cook-ups in my kitchen from time to time.

Search "recipes" on **heartfoundation.org.au** for easy, healthy options.

JANUARY 28

BLUE IS PROVEN TO BOOST CREATIVITY, SO SURROUND YOURSELF WITH THE COLOUR TODAY. WEAR BLUE, SPEND TIME LOOKING AT THE SKY OR THE SEA, AND SEEK OUT BLUE WHEREVER YOU GO.

List five things you saw today that were blue.

1. _____

2. _____

3. _____

4. _____

5. _____

Lisa's Musing

Now let me tell you, this one is a breath of fresh air for me. Fun fact: I wore pink for about five years. I was obsessed. I even called one of my first companies Pinque, and my first two book covers were entirely pink. So blue – let's do this! (It suits me much better anyway.)

My sannyasin name is Sagara, which means ocean. While I don't wear much blue, I spend most of my time by or in the ocean. It feeds my soul. That name was given to me in Pune, India, by a guru who knew nothing about me. Intuition and the universe doing its best work.

TAKE A LONG BATH AND LISTEN TO A TED TALK OR PODCAST THAT SPEAKS TO YOUR CREATIVITY.

Bath checklist: essential oils, phone notifications off, candles, bath soak, face mask, glass of wine (optional). Use the space below to journal how you feel after your bath. Did you have any creative ideas?

_____

_____

_____

_____

_____

_____

Lisa's Musing

The beauty of all of this wonderful content is that it doesn't have to cost you a cent. There is so much wonderful information out there for us now to help us unwind, relax and be more mindful every day.

Choose a talk at **ted.com** or check out my very own Hear me RAW podcast on Apple or Spotify. To take your bath to the next level, check out **@solitudebodymind** bath cookies and relaxing bath ritual meditations.

JANUARY 30

VISIT AN ART SUPPLIES STORE, EVEN IF YOU DON'T CONSIDER YOURSELF AN ARTIST, AND TAKE IN THE COLOURS, OBJECTS AND IDEAS. CONSIDER BUYING SOMETHING TO TRY - PERHAPS A CALLIGRAPHY PEN OR WATERCOLOUR PAD - AND SPEND SOME TIME EXPERIMENTING WITH IT. BE KIND TO YOURSELF: NO ONE IS BORN A SKILLED ARTIST. IT TAKES PRACTICE.

Who are the artists you admire?

1. _____

2. _____

3. _____

4. _____

5. _____

I did a wonderful painting class with **corkandcanvas.com.au** as a surprise 'date night' recently with my fiancé. We had an absolute ball. Neither of us are particularly artistic in this way, yet we both managed to walk out with relatively fabulous paintings of jellyfish! And at age 70, my mum picked up a paintbrush for practically the first time in her life. Now there's no stopping her. It's become one of her absolute favorite pursuits and she's super talented at it.

Try **artfuladdict.com** and **paintplot.com.au**. Also, watch this space for a special *Collective Hub* paint by numbers releasing soon!

JANUARY 31

CREATIVITY IS A SKILL THAT NEEDS PRACTISING. CONTINUAL LEARNING IS THE KEY. SIGN UP FOR A CREATIVE CLASS, OR EVEN JUST A CREATIVE EXPERIENCE, THAT PUTS YOU OUT OF YOUR COMFORT ZONE. IF YOU LIKE MUSIC, TRY POTTERY; IF YOU LIKE TO DOODLE, TRY DANCE. PUSHING YOUR CREATIVE BOUNDARIES WILL HAVE FAR-REACHING CONSEQUENCES.

What creative actions will you commit to in the future?

_____

_____

_____

_____

_____

_____

Lisa's Musing

What a month! A massive huge high five and kudos to you.
How do you feel? I can't wait to hear what your favourite activity
for the month was. Be sure to let me know, and follow along on
my journey too. We're all in this together!

*"Creativity involves breaking out of expected patterns in
order to look at things in a different way."* – Edward de Bono

february

GET MOVING

You knew exercise was in this book somewhere, didn't you!

That's because moving your body is one of the greatest things you can do to improve your health. Fitness is the greatest natural antidepressant around, so why not overdose on it?

The next 28 days will be all about increasing the movement you do every day. And it's not just about fitting in that extra boxing class or running an extra 5km, it's about moving more in everyday activities, and moving more often, too.

We spend most of our lives sitting down doing work or lying down and sleeping. Let's bring a little of that movement back, day by day, until it's just a way of life. As it should be.

We promise you'll feel fitter, happier and healthier in no time.

LET'S START THIS CHALLENGE BY BEING MINDFUL OF HOW WE MOVE. TAKE NOTE OF YOUR MOVEMENTS TODAY; ARE THERE TIMES YOU TAKE SHORTCUTS OR AVOID DOING EXTRA MOVEMENTS? USE THE STEP COUNTER ON YOUR PHONE OR SMART WATCH TO TRACK HOW MANY STEPS YOU TAKE TODAY. YES, THIS IS OBVIOUS, BUT IT GIVES YOU A GOOD STARTING NUMBER TO IMPROVE UPON EACH DAY. WALKING MORE IS AN INCREDIBLY EFFECTIVE CHANGE WE CAN ALL EASILY MAKE TO OUR HEALTH.

Write down what changes you made today. How many steps did you take?

_____

_____

_____

_____

_____

Lisa's Musing

My good friend Lorna Jane Clarkson taught me that incremental bits of exercise really help. For example, rather than taking an escalator, take the steps. I've trained my brain to always look for the harder way and take no shortcuts. Your step counter may surprise you.

Some great smart watches and step counters include Fitbit Inspire, Samsung Galaxy Watch, Apple Watch and Garmin. Or you could use a simple digital pedometer.

START THE DAY WITH CHILD'S POSE (KNEES FOLDED UNDERNEATH YOU, HEAD ON THE FLOOR, AND ARMS EITHER BY YOUR SIDES OR STRETCHED OUT IN FRONT) FOR TWO MINUTES, AND AGAIN AT NIGHT BEFORE BED. IT SOUNDS COUNTERINTUITIVE, AS YOU WON'T BE MOVING IN THIS POSE, BUT IT'S A GREAT WAY TO STRETCH YOUR BACK, RELAX YOUR NECK AND PRACTICE CARVING OUT TIME DEVOTED TO YOUR BODY.

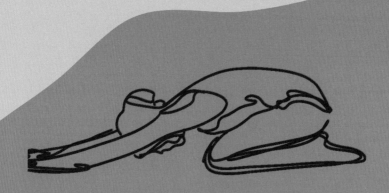

Lisa's musing

This pose is so relaxing! I often do this in front of the TV or after a shower. I just try to drop down a few times and soak it up.

"Yoga is the fountain of youth. You're only as young as your spine is flexible." – Bob Harper

NOW FOCUS ON ONE OF OUR MOST USED (AND ABUSED!) BODY AREAS: THE NECK AND SHOULDERS. BEGIN BY MOVING YOUR HEAD FROM LEFT TO RIGHT, AND UP AND DOWN, FOR FIVE MINUTES. THEN ROLL YOUR SHOULDERS BACKWARDS AND FORWARDS. TIP YOUR HEAD FORWARDS AND REST YOUR HANDS ON THE BACK OF THE NECK TO RELEASE TENSION. DO THIS SEVERAL TIMES THROUGHOUT THE DAY.

At the end of the day, write down how you feel... Do you feel more calm? Relaxed? Are your neck and shoulders feeling more free?

Lisa's Musing

Doing it as I write. So simple. So good.

Follow my gorgeous friend **@shona_vertue**.
She has some wonderful, simple mobility exercises.

TIME TO WORK YOUR LOWER BACK WITH BRIDGE POSE. LIE ON YOUR BACK WITH ARMS BY YOUR SIDES, KNEES BENT, AND FEET FLAT ON THE FLOOR. SLOWLY RAISE YOUR HIPS, CONTRACTING YOUR GLUTES AND HAMSTRINGS AS YOU GO. KEEP SHOULDERS ON THE FLOOR. HOLD FOR 10-15 SECONDS, THEN REPEAT FIVE TIMES. YOUR GLUTES WILL LOVE THIS MOVE.

Liza's musing

I have a funny reaction to bridge pose. It's like I get this sudden rush of energy (almost to the point of discomfort) where I feel like I need to get up and run to expend it. We all react and respond differently to different things and that's okay. You do you. But notice consciously what goes on for you personally as you work through each exercise.

Want to be inspired? Follow **@sjanaelise,** **@traveling_yogigirl** and **@lottasebzdayoga.**

SUGGEST A WALKING MEETING OR PHONE CALL TODAY AND CHOOSE A NEW PATH TO EXPLORE. YOU MIGHT FIND YOUR HEART RACING, BUT YOU'LL BE ABLE TO FOCUS BETTER THAN SITTING IN FRONT OF YOUR COMPUTER.

Walking checklist: comfy shoes and clothes, water, healthy snack, earplugs with microphone... Plan your next walking meetings in the space below!

_____

_____

_____

_____

_____

_____

Lisa's Musing

Walking meetings are one of my all-time fave things to do. If time is our only finite resource, why not double up and knock off a meeting while doing an hour of walking? I'm lucky enough to live in Bondi, Sydney, just near the Bondi to Bronte walk, but when I travel I love getting lost in the back streets or discovering new paths or walkways.

"All truly great thoughts are conceived by walking."
– Friedrich Nietzsche

INSTEAD OF EATING AT YOUR DESK OR IN THE KITCHEN, MAKE A SPECIAL EFFORT TO EAT OUTSIDE TODAY. MAYBE HEAD TO THE PARK OR A NEARBY CAFE. IT'S A SIMPLE WAY TO GET MORE MOVEMENT INTO YOUR DAY.

Before lunch: how do you feel? Are you carrying
any tension? What are you worried about?
After lunch: do you feel less stressed? Are your neck
and shoulders tense? How do you feel?

_____

_____

_____

_____

_____

Lisa's Musing

Guilty as charged. I know first-hand how tricky it can be to take a break when you're on a roll. I get so into my work that I have to consciously remove myself from my desk and go outside. I promise I'll do it from here on in!

If you're short on time, you could subscribe to a healthy food delivery service in advance, such as Soulara or Hello Fresh.

LEGS UP: LIE ON THE FLOOR WITH YOUR LEGS EXTENDED UPWARDS AND RESTING AGAINST A WALL. THIS POSE WILL ENCOURAGE BLOOD FLOW AND LYMPH DRAINAGE TOWARDS YOUR HEART.

Lisa's Musing

This feels SO good. I remember one night dancing so hard for so long at a party that I literally lay down in the hallway with my legs up against the wall (stone cold sober, I might add). Pretty soon I was joined by about 10 other people! It's one of the most fun memories I have. Be unafraid to be yourself, wherever you are. It doesn't have to be just reserved for home.

"Yoga means addition. Addition of energy, strength and beauty to body, mind and soul." – Amit Ray

FIND 10 MINUTES TODAY AND PLANT YOUR TOES ON THE EDGE OF A STEP AND SLOWLY LET YOUR HEELS DIP DOWN. REMEMBER THOSE? THEY'RE YOUR CALVES! THAT MAJOR MUSCLE WE ALWAYS FORGET ABOUT.

Want to build strong calves? Skipping is a great way to build calf muscles and it'll get your heart pumping too. How else can you get your legs moving today? List your plan below.

_____

_____

_____

_____

_____

Lisa's Musing

Oh, I can feel it as I write this! It's so, so simple but so, so good. And we can do this anywhere. Any time. No equipment needed.

For more stretching ideas, download a stretching and flexibility app so you can do them easily at home.

EVERY TIME YOU CHECK YOUR EMAIL OR SOCIAL MEDIA ON YOUR PHONE TODAY, HOVER IN A SQUAT POSITION. IT'LL HELP YOU RAISE YOUR HEARTBEAT AND WILL INEVITABLY KEEP YOUR SCREEN TIME DOWN!

You can also try balancing on one foot. Warning: it'll be challenging. What other things can you do during squat time? List them below and remember to share them with us so we can try them too!

Lisa's musing

My squat form over the years went from great to terrible. So this one's for me as much as you. 1) Stand with your feet a little wider than hip width. 2) Pop your hips back, bending at the knees and ankles. 3) Sit into a squat position with your feet driving down; chest up, shoulders back. 4) Aim to be parallel with your knees bent to 90 degrees.

"Don't have $100 shoes and a 10 cent squat." – Louie Simmons

FEBRUARY 10

FIND SOME GREENERY TODAY TO RELAX IN. SPENDING TIME IN PARKS, FORESTS, EVEN BY THE BEACH NATURALLY ENCOURAGES YOU TO MOVE MORE. TAKE SOME DEEP BREATHS, AVOID YOUR PHONE, AND EXPLORE.

Spend time looking for beautiful leaves, perfect blades of grass, colourful flowers. Paste, trace or draw them here.

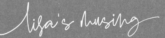

Earthing yourself is so simple, so free and relaxing. Take your shoes off. Remove technology and just soak it up.

"Adopt the pace of nature. Her secret is patience."
– Ralph Waldo Emerson

LET'S BUST OUT THE PLANK! THIS POSE IS SO GREAT FOR YOUR CORE AND YOUR FOCUS. FIVE TIMES TODAY, HOLD A PLANK POSITION FOR ONE MINUTE. FITNESS LOVERS: AIM TO DOUBLE THE LENGTH OF YOUR PLANK EACH ROUND. IF YOU CAN'T QUITE MAINTAIN THE PLANK, DROP TO YOUR KNEES FOR THE REMAINDER OF THE MINUTE, BUT DO NOT GIVE UP!

Describe how your body felt during the plank and afterwards. What muscles are strong, what muscles do you need to work on, and what muscles are sore?

_____

_____

_____

_____

Lisa's Musing

Okay, so this is one exercise you can get super good at quite easily. Fun fact: in 2019, I shared the stage with Sir Richard Branson twice. He is well known for asking people he's with to drop and give him a 'plank off,' so I was ready. Oh boy, was I ready. I planked every day for a month to train, and it felt good to have one solid skill – albeit not that useful in day-to-day life.

Remember, don't give up because you think you've hit a wall. Just focus on the idea of progress.

TODAY IS A FUN ONE! GIVE A FRIEND PERMISSION TO TEXT YOU RANDOMLY FOUR TIMES THROUGH THE DAY WITH ONE OF THE FOLLOWING ACTIONS: DANCE, SQUAT, STAR JUMPS, HOP. THEN, WHEREVER YOU ARE, STOP AND DO THE MOVE FOR BETWEEN 30 SECONDS AND 1 MINUTE. YOU MAY LOOK FUNNY DOING IT IN THE POST OFFICE OR AT YOUR WORKSPACE, BUT IT'LL MAKE YOU SMILE AND GET YOU MOVING WHEN YOU LEAST EXPECT IT.

Think of some other commands and write them down here. Next time you can pick different friends and do this again and again and again!

So much fun. Trust me. Sounds bonkers, but this morning I told my niece she could give me these commands at any time today. We had SO much fun. Laughed our lungs out.

Got a video from today? We'd love to see it #collectivehub or post it in our Facebook group! If you haven't signed up to our closed wellness group yet, do it now – search Collective Hub Club and request to join!

TODAY WE'LL WORK YOUR CORE AND CONCENTRATION. BEFORE YOU EAT YOUR MEALS TODAY, BALANCE IN TREE POSE FOR TWO MINUTES (A MINUTE ON EACH FOOT). THE KEY IS TO FOCUS ON A SPOT ON THE WALL TO HELP YOU BALANCE. THIS IS ALSO A GREAT MINDFUL EXERCISE IF YOU ARE STRESSED.

Lisa's musing

Balance is so important. It's something I'm really working on and, to be honest, not great at… but practice makes perfect. Consistency is key.

"There's a crack in everything, that's how the light gets in."
– Leonard Cohen

CARDIO EXERCISE HAS MORE BENEFITS THAN YOU CAN POKE A STICK AT, BUT NOT EVERYONE LOVES IT. TODAY, EXPLORE SOME FUN WAYS TO GET YOUR HEART PUMPING FOR 30 MINUTES OR MORE: TRAMPOLINING, HULA HOOPING, DANCING, OR IF YOU'RE A CARDIO LOVER, GET DOWN WITH YOUR BURPEES AND STAIR SPRINTS! YOUR HEART WILL THANK YOU FOR IT.

Write down five different, fun ways to raise your heartbeat:

Lisa's musing

I have a general rule I live by, which is to be fit enough to be able to do pretty much anything at any time. I always want to 'live my life out loud,' so I made a promise to myself that I'd keep my cardio up so that I'm ready for anything. I never, ever want to say, "Oh, I can't do that." I want to be able to do it all.

Some great apps for this are Zova and Centr.

FEBRUARY 15

STRETCH THOSE SORE MUSCLES TODAY! TREAT YOURSELF TO A FULL 15 MINUTES IN THE MORNING AND THE EVENING. FOCUS ON YOUR LEGS, BACK AND NECK. DID YOU KNOW THAT STRETCHING IS ALSO GREAT FOR YOUR MIND? IT RELEASES ENDORPHINS, REDUCES STRESS AND CALMS TENSIONS. IT'S LIKE A MOVING MEDITATION.

Write down all the stretches you completed today so you
have them for reference when you do them next.

Stretching is just so good for you, and you can do it anywhere, any
time. I often just lie down on my back, raise my legs and alternate my
knees across my body to release my back. There are so many simple
ways to stretch, and your body (and your mind) will thank you for it.

Check out Morning Stretch Routine by my good
friend Shona Vertue on YouTube.

FEBRUARY 16

WATCH ONE OF YOUR FAVOURITE EPISODES OF *FRIENDS*, AND EVERY TIME SOMEONE SAYS MONICA, CHANDLER, RACHEL, JOEY, PHOEBE OR ROSS, DO FIVE SIT-UPS AND FIVE SQUATS. MORE OF A *GOSSIP GIRL* OR SATC FAN? DO THE SAME WITH WHEN ANY OF THE MAIN CHARACTERS ARE NAMED.

Does watching this show remind you of a
time in your life? Write about it below:

_____

_____

_____

_____

_____

_____

Lisa's musing

Sometimes you've got to throw a little fun into your workouts.
The trick is to show up consistently, but then find different, enjoyable
ways to keep you excited and engaged.

*"Fitness is not about being better than someone else.
It's about being better than you used to be."* – Khloé Kardashian

LACE UP! IF YOU'RE NEW TO RUNNING, START SLOW WITH A STRETCH AND A SLOW 2-3KM JOG. IF YOU'RE A RUNNING PRO, RUN FOR 20-30 MINUTES, ADDING IN A ONE-MINUTE SPRINT (AS FAST AS YOU CAN GO) EVERY FIVE MINUTES. GET THAT HEART RATE PUMPING!

How did you feel before this run? How did you feel afterwards?

lisa's musing

I am really not a runner. However, last year I bought myself a treadmill (much to my bookkeeper's horror as I bought one in 2014 and never used it). I'm pleased to say I've used it at least three times a week and have gone from dreading it to absolutely loving it! I have a killer Spotify playlist (mostly '80s and '90s remixes,) and I play a game where I push myself a little further every time. I'm up to 6km now. I run at 10 or 11 for a minute, then take a 30-second break, all the way through. Works for me!

There are so many great apps to try: **@runhunters** – for runners who like exploring. **@runningheroesaunz** – run and get rewarded. **@nikerunning** – a running club with guided runs.

TRY A NEW FITNESS CLASS TODAY WITH A FRIEND. CHOOSE ONE THAT WILL CHALLENGE YOU A LITTLE: BOXING, PILATES, HOT YOGA. DOING IT WITH A FRIEND WILL MAKE IT EASIER AND YOU'LL BE LESS LIKELY TO CANCEL!

Before: What are your thoughts about this class you are about to do?

Afterwards: How did your preconceptions compare to the reality of this class?

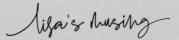

Alternatively, if you have home equipment, invite a friend to join you at home or in the park. I bought myself some inexpensive boxing gloves and mitts from Kmart and sometimes I'll grab a friend and do a fun, 20-minute workout together.

"Do something today that your future self will thank you for."
– Sean Patrick Flanery

PICK YOUR FAVOURITE '90S TUNE AND MAKE UP A DANCE ROUTINE TO IT. YES, WE'RE SERIOUS. REMEMBER HOW FUN THIS WAS WHEN YOU WERE 12? CHANNEL THAT ENERGY AND HAVE A LAUGH.

Why is this your favourite song? What memories are attached to it?

_____

_____

_____

_____

_____

_____

_____

_____

_____

Lisa's Musing

What can I say, I love all things Jane Fonda. Her workouts, movies, books… an absolutely talented legend of a lady.

～～～～

Check out '90s Dance Hits on Spotify.

GRAB THREE PAIRS OF ROLLED UP SOCKS AND LEARN TO JUGGLE! WHY? WELL, APART FROM IMPRESSING FRIENDS AT DINNER PARTIES, JUGGLING IS A GREAT WORKOUT FOR YOUR CORE AND YOUR FOCUS, PLUS IT'S A STRESS RELIEVER. ALREADY KNOW HOW? INTRODUCE ANOTHER BALL AND GET REALLY TRICKY.

Draw a picture that represents your juggling experience. I can't wait to see these! Tag us #collectivehub or post a pic of this page to our Facebook group: Collective Hub Club.

Lisa's Musing

Oh my gosh. This was harder than I remembered! Years ago someone gave me some juggling balls for my birthday and I thought I'd mastered it. Turns out it's not quite as simple as 'getting back on the horse,' but lots of fun. Good luck!

Search "how to juggle" on YouTube for video instructions.

BACK TO MUSCLES! DO A WALL SIT (LEANING AGAINST A WALL WITH YOUR KNEES AT A 90-DEGREE ANGLE, FEET PLANTED ON THE FLOOR) THREE TIMES TODAY. SEE HOW LONG YOU CAN HOLD THE POSE FOR. NEXT LEVEL? GRAB A WEIGHT (OR A HEAVY COFFEE TABLE BOOK) AND PLACE IT ON TOP OF YOUR QUADS). ENJOY THE 'GOOD' PAIN TOMORROW!

How long did you last each of the three times?

_____

_____

_____

_____

_____

_____

_____

Lisa's Musing

It sounds so simple, but just try it and feel the BURN.

Tip: Don't forget to wear supportive trainers for this, even if you're doing it on carpet. Your feet and ankles will need the extra support.

TEST YOURSELF WITH SOME STANDING LONG JUMPS. MARK A LINE ON THE FLOOR AND, WITH NO RUN-UP, JUMP WITH BOTH FEET AS FAR AS YOU CAN. MEASURE YOUR JUMP AND TRY TO IMPROVE ON IT NEXT TIME. DO THIS TWICE, FIRST THING IN THE MORNING AND THEN AT NIGHT. WHEN IS YOUR LONGEST JUMP AND HOW FAR IS IT?

How did you go?

Record your scores below

Morning
Rep 1:
Rep 2:

Evening
Rep 1:
Rep 2:

I haven't done long jumps since school. It's funny how writing something can transport you back to a time in your life. I can still feel the sand under my feet as I land.

Check out **jumpandclimb.com.au** for some of the benefits of jumping.

PRACTISE A SERIES OF YOGA POSES OUTSIDE IN YOUR FAVOURITE PARK, BEACH OR NATURE RESERVE. DON'T CHEAT AND DO THIS IN YOUR LIVING ROOM – THE IDEA IS TO FOCUS ON YOUR POSES AND YOUR BREATHING, WHILE ENJOYING THE SIGHTS AND SMELLS OF NATURE. TAKE A PHOTO AND SHARE IT WITH US: #COLLECTIVEHUB, OR POST IT IN OUR FACEBOOK GROUP, COLLECTIVE HUB CLUB!

Yoga essentials: make sure your posture is correct, your core is engaged, and that you stop if you feel any pain. Use the space below to note what moves you worked on today and how you felt you did them.

_____

_____

_____

_____

_____

_____

Lisa's musing

My mum is in her mid-70s, and every morning (no excuses) she does a 20-minute self-guided yoga routine. She also does classes twice a week, and is, without a doubt, the most fit and flexible person I know.

For some poses to try, check out: **yogajournal.com/poses**.

FEBRUARY 24

SPEND TIME TODAY TOUCHING YOUR TOES, THEN STRETCH UP AND TRY TO TOUCH THE CLOUDS. REPEAT 5-10 TIMES IN THE MORNING AND AGAIN IN THE EVENING, BREATHING SLOWLY AS YOU DO THEM.

Did your flexibility change from morning to night?

Did you find the deep breathing a stress buster?

Lisa's Musing

About 10 years ago, before I started training pretty religiously, I could not touch my toes. If feels nuts and almost a little embarrassing writing that now, as I plant my palms firmly on the floor. My point? I'm a lot older now, yet a hell of a lot stronger and fitter. It doesn't matter what stage you're at – just start. You will see incremental improvements.

For inspiration, follow sports physician
@odetteblacklock on Instagram.

@COLLECTIVEHUB #COLLECTIVEHUB

HOLD A PRIVATE SILENT DISCO TONIGHT FOR 10-15 MINUTES BEFORE YOU GO TO BED. TURN OFF ALL THE LIGHTS, TURN YOUR EARPHONES TO MAX, FIND YOUR FAVOURITE PLAYLIST AND JUST DANCE.

Write down a favourite memory that involved dancing.

_____

_____

_____

_____

_____

_____

_____

Lisa's Musing

The BEST! If you could see me in my living room/kitchen/bedroom, most days I have my own private disco. I love to dance anywhere, any time. Unashamedly. I have been known to dance in queues, in the supermarket – you name it, I will dance it out. It's my all-time go-to feel-good move. When in doubt, dance it out, I say!

Want to learn some moves? Try **groovetherapy101.com**.

FEBRUARY 26

TIME TO RAMP IT UP. FIVE TIMES THROUGHOUT TODAY, SEE HOW MANY LUNGES YOU CAN DO IN ONE MINUTE. DOESN'T SOUND THAT HARD? YOU WILL FEEL YOUR MUSCLES TOMORROW MORNING! FOR FITNESS LOVERS, TRY TO BEAT YOUR NUMBER BY 10 PER CENT EACH TIME.

Write down the number of lunges you managed to do

1. _____

2. _____

3. _____

4. _____

5. _____

Lisa's Musing

When you're doing this, make sure you align your knees and have everything in line with your feet. I did some lunges about eight months ago and let my left knee wobble out to the side, and hurt it quite a bit. It took me about seven months to get it feeling strong again. So always go with caution and focus on technique, rather than speed.

"Strength doesn't come from what you can do. It comes from overcoming the things you once thought you couldn't." – Rikki Rogers

NOW FOR A REAL PUSH TO END THE MONTH. BRING OUT THE BURPEES! YES, THEY SUCK – BUT THEY SUCK FOR A GREAT REASON: THEY WORK YOUR ENTIRE BODY IN ONE MOVE. SEE HOW MANY BURPEES YOU CAN DO IN TWO MINUTES WITHOUT STOPPING. DO THIS THREE TIMES TODAY.

How did you go?

Record your scores below:

Rep 1:

Rep 2:

Rep 3:

Lisa's Musing

My trainer Todd is doing 180 burpees a day as I'm writing this. In Australia eight lives are lost to suicide every day, and the majority are men. Todd's 180 burpees represent the 180 male lives lost per month. Find a cause and get behind it. It will give you a reason to train.

"The pain you feel today will be the strength you feel tomorrow."
– Arnold Schwarzenegger

FEBRUARY 28

GIVE YOUR MUSCLES A SPA TONIGHT BY SOAKING IN EPSOM SALTS, WHICH CONTAIN A MUSCLE RELAXANT. LIGHT A CANDLE, AVOID YOUR PHONE, AND CHILL.

To help you reach maximum chill, list five things you can do to switch off, such as choosing a playlist or a meditation, reading a book, or just closing your eyes and thinking about how grateful you are. Remember to put your phone on 'do not disturb' so you can really switch off.

1. _____

2. _____

3. _____

4. _____

5. _____

Lisa's Musing

So simple. So inexpensive. If you don't have a bath, pour some water in a bucket and give your feet a long soak. Or, if you're like me, have a list of non-negotiables when you move house. A bath has always been one of my top priorities, behind natural light and lots of air.

～～～～～～～

Some of my fave bath salts are from Salt By Hendrix, Epzen and French Girl.

What did you love about this month and what have you learned?

_____
_____
_____
_____
_____
_____
_____
_____
_____
_____
_____
_____
_____
_____

march

EAT THE RAINBOW

We know, we know... healthy eating can be challenging when you're running a business, have a family and/or have a side hustle. And that's why we want to focus on what goes into our body this month.

The thing about eating food is that it's the fuel that helps our body and brain to function (that's a no-brainer, right?). But the fact of the matter is, without nutrients, the machines that are our bodies have nothing to run on.

And that results in those feelings of exhaustion in our body, lack of focus in our mind, and even an extra layer of love on our hips.

So, let's dive right in.

DO YOU KNOW WHAT YOU EAT? SOUNDS LIKE AN OBVIOUS QUESTION, BUT TRY TO KEEP A FOOD AND DRINK DIARY TODAY TO SEE EXACTLY WHAT YOU EAT ON A NORMAL DAY. WHERE COULD YOU INCORPORATE MORE VEGETABLES AND WHERE COULD YOU CUT DOWN A LITTLE?

List all the foods/drinks you ate today:

Breakfast	Lunch	Dinner	Snacks

Lisa's Musing

It's the perfect time for me to be writing this. Recently, my personal trainer asked me to keep a food diary. It keeps us accountable and makes us think a little more consciously about what we put in our mouths. If we know we need to share it with someone else, it makes us all the more honest. One thing I'm doing for the month is cutting out sugar completely and drinking a lot more water. Feel free to share your food diary with me, so we can all support each other.

"Writing down everything that you put in your mouth really helps. I don't count a damn calorie. But when I'm really trying to eat healthy, I write everything down. It really holds me accountable and puts me on a healthier path." – Tyra Banks

LOOKING AT YOUR FOOD DIARY FROM YESTERDAY, PICK TWO TO THREE 'BAD' EATING HABITS THAT YOU'D LIKE TO TURN AROUND. IT MIGHT BE YOUR SNACKING, LACK OF WATER INTAKE OR MAYBE JUST A LOVE OF CHOCOLATE THAT'S GONE WILD (DITTO). COMMIT TO CURBING THOSE THIS MONTH.

Write down these habits, and strategies you can use to limit them.

_____

_____

_____

_____

_____

_____

Lisa's musing

Oh, how good is this?! Chances are, purely by doing the exercise yesterday, you might have already started to turn around some little habits that have snuck in. I'm proud of you. You're doing great. And just know that I am right there with you on this journey!

"Let food be thy medicine and thy medicine be food." – Hippocrates

IT'S TIME TO CLEAN OUT YOUR FRIDGE. CHECK ALL THE EXPIRY AND BEST BEFORE DATES, MAKE SOME TOUGH CALLS ON ANYTHING THAT HAS A LOT OF SALT, SUGAR OR FAT IN IT, AND PLACE ALL THE HEALTHY SNACK FRIENDLY FOODS WHERE YOU CAN SEE THEM.

Let's get real. What food items are you struggling to throw out?

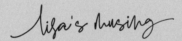

Let me tell you, for someone who is slightly on the 'hoarding' end of the spectrum (I don't like to waste a thing) throwing stuff out is really tricky for me to do. So here's what I've done. Everything that is sugary or on the naughty side and might tempt me, I gift in a big box to my mother-in-law (make it someone else's problem!). Then I make sure all the out-of-date stuff goes straight in the bin. Now, how good does that feel?

"Sorry, there's no magic bullet. You gotta eat healthy and live healthy to be healthy and look healthy. End of story." – Morgan Spurlock

HALF THE CHALLENGE OF HEALTHY EATING IS HAVING HEALTHY FOOD ON HAND. DO SOME RESEARCH AND PICK FIVE EASY, HEALTHY MEALS THAT YOU CAN FREEZE. PLAN YOUR SHOPPING LIST AND SET ASIDE SOME TIME TO MAKE THEM. PREPPING IS KEY.

Five meals I will prepare:

1.

2.

3.

4.

5.

The snacks I will make:

Lisa's musing

I am my own worst enemy when I get 'hangry'. That's when I tend to grab whatever's around, and then promptly beat myself up afterwards. So now I plan ahead. What am I going to eat when? What healthy snacks do I have in my fridge and pantry? What do I need to throw in my bag so I don't get tempted? It's all in the planning.

For inspo, follow these dietitians on Instagram: Dr Megan Rossi from @theguthealthdoctor, Kiah Paetz from @theplantbased_dietitian, Taylor Ryan from @the_sportsdietitian and Maeve Hanan from @dieteticallyspeaking.

MARCH 5

DO A GENERAL SHOP TODAY WITH YOUR LIST FROM YESTERDAY. STOCK UP ON FRUIT, VEGETABLES AND HEALTHY FOODS. SET YOURSELF UP FOR A MONTH OF HEALTHY EATING! FREEZE EVERYTHING IN PORTIONS AND WRITE A LIST ON YOUR FRIDGE OF WHAT'S THERE. MARK OFF EACH PORTION AS YOU EAT IT SO YOU KNOW WHEN YOU NEED TO DO ANOTHER SHOP.

My shopping list:

_____   _____   _____   _____

_____   _____   _____   _____

_____   _____   _____   _____

_____   _____   _____   _____

_____   _____   _____   _____

Lisa's Musing

This is really tricky at the start, so let's change our mindset. Set yourself some goals about why you're doing this: how do you want to feel, what weight do you want to be, how much energy do you want to have, for example. Then suddenly it becomes like a game, a little competition with yourself. Whenever I do this, rather than feeling overwhelmed or bored with the idea, I start to get excited by it.

A recent study found that only 5 per cent of Aussies eat the recommended amount of fruit and veg!

MARCH 6

IT'S TIME TO STAY HYDRATED. DON'T ROLL YOUR EYES! STUDIES SHOW THAT 80 PER CENT OF US STILL AREN'T DRINKING ENOUGH WATER. AIM FOR YOUR EIGHT OR SO GLASSES TODAY, WITH THESE NON-BORING WATER INFUSION COMBOS: BLACKBERRY AND LEMON, WATERMELON AND BASIL, ORANGE AND ROSEMARY, STRAWBERRY AND MINT GREEN TEA. LET THEM SOAK UP THE FLAVOURS IN A JUG IN THE FRIDGE FOR AN HOUR OR SO BEFORE SERVING.

Think of some other combinations that you might like and list them here:

_____

_____

_____

_____

_____

Lisa's musing

I am terrible at drinking enough water. I'm the first to admit it. To combat this, I have a one-litre bottle (buy yourself one that you love) on my desk or with me at all times. And I ensure that I get through at least two full ones a day.

Looking for a beautiful water bottle to help you stay hydrated? Check out **biome.com.au, earthbottles.com.au** and **corkcicle.com** as well as **The Iconic** and **Rebel Sport**.

**TRY A NEW FRUIT OR VEGETABLE TODAY. GET CREATIVE AND
FIND AN EASY RECIPE TO EASE YOU INTO THIS MONTH.**

Have you tried these: Broccolini? Star fruit? Taro? Turnip? Dragon fruit?
List all the fruits or veggies you've never eaten and pick one to try today.

_____

_____

_____

_____

_____

_____

Lisa's Musing

Make this Fun with a capital F! I do this by either going to visit a
different local produce market to discover something new, or ordering
a random online box of mixed veggie goodness. This just shakes it up
a bit and keeps it fresh. Take it one step further and organise a dinner
party or picnic where everyone needs to bring a dish using something
that they've never used before. How fun and adventurous!

Looking for a veggie box? Try **doorsteporganics.com.au,
organicbox.com.au** and **yordar.com.au.**

MARCH 8

PROTEIN IS IMPORTANT TO HELP US FEEL FULL, REDUCING OUR NEED FOR SNACKS, AND IT CAN HELP WITH LOWERING BLOOD PRESSURE TOO. EXPERIMENT TODAY WITH ADDING VEGETABLE PROTEIN TO EACH MEAL – TRY QUINOA, LENTILS, BEANS, YOGHURT, TOFU OR EVEN BUCKWHEAT (WHICH IS LIKE A CHUNKY RICE).

List the meals you can make using the above ingredients. Take a pic and tag us #collectivehub, or post it in our private Facebook group (Collective Hub Club) to inspire others with your creations.

_____

_____

_____

_____

_____

Lisa's musing

Here's the funny thing. As I'm writing this chapter I've been off sugar for seven days, and so the thought of these things is actually making me salivate. Our bodies adjust remarkably quickly, and one of my faves at the moment is farrow.

~~~~~~~

Good sources of plant-based protein include:
chia seeds 6-9g (3 tbsp), almonds 15g (½ cup), chickpeas 7.5g (½ cup), peas 4g (½ cup), hemp seeds 10g (3 tbsp).

THE PACKAGED FOOD WE EAT TENDS TO HAVE A LOT OF INGREDIENTS. TODAY LOOK AT THE INGREDIENTS PANEL OF EVERYTHING YOU EAT. TAKE NOTE OF THINGS LIKE SUGAR, SALT, TRANS FATS, ETC. LOOK FOR 5G PER 100G FOR SUGAR, 3G PER 100G OF SALT AND LITTLE TO NO TRANS FATS.

Have a look at the back of your favourite packaged food and list the ingredients that worry you. What foods should you give up?

_____

_____

_____

_____

_____

Lisa's musing

Oh the horror. I remember the first time I did this, I felt downright deflated. There is so much crap in everything we consume. But after a while I started to train myself. Then I went one step further, and now I try to avoid as much packaged food as possible. There is a general rule of thumb my mum taught me growing up in the country: if it grows from the ground or falls from a tree then it's good to eat. Avoid packaged and processed foods where possible.

For a guide, check out **eatforhealth.gov.au, nutritionaustralia.org/fact-sheets, mydailyintake.net**.

LOVE CARBS? WE HEAR YA! A LOT OF THE CARBS WE EAT ARE REFINED IN SOME WAY, HAVE LITTLE TO NO NUTRITIONAL VALUE, AND LACK FIBRE. SWAP THEM OUT TODAY FOR BETTER VERSIONS. YOU'LL BE AMAZED AT HOW MUCH MORE FULL YOU'LL FEEL.

Write down the carbs you swapped and what healthy alternatives you chose:

List your carb below:

Now, list your healthy alternative:

Lisa's musing

As I'm writing this I've gone off all sugar and all bad carbs. It's tough. I *love* bread. And I love potatoes. But I'm consciously finding other ways to include carbs in my daily intake. I'm feeling fitter and stronger as a result. And the more I go into it, the less I feel like the bad stuff.

"Is butter a carb?" – Regina, Mean Girls.

IT'S TIME TO START CLEAN EATING! SOUNDS SCARY, BUT ACTUALLY IT JUST MEANS EATING REAL FOOD. SPEND TODAY EATING EVERYTHING FRESH: NO PACKAGED FOODS OR ANYTHING FROM A TIN. JUST GOOD OLD VEGGIES AND FRUIT IN THEIR FRESHEST FORM FOR EVERY MEAL. SEE HOW IT IMPROVES YOUR DIGESTION.

A smoothie is a great way to do this. Here's the perfect smoothie recipe:

Step 1. Grab two BIG handfuls of fresh baby spinach leaves.

Step 2. Add a fresh banana and/or mango.

Step 3. Add a glass of water.

Step 4. The extras: add in some fresh mint, strawberries, blueberries and raspberries. Viola! A perfectly natural smoothie.

Lisa's Musing

I am committed to a super clean eating journey.
Trust me, it's worth it.

Love your veggies? Consider having your own little garden full of them. Vegepod (**vegepod.com.au**) does an awesome job for those with small gardens or renters.

SUGAR BE GONE! REFINED SUGAR HAS BEEN LINKED TO HEART DISEASE, DEPRESSION AND OBESITY. TODAY, CUT OUT ANYTHING WITH REFINED SUGAR. AND WE MEAN *ANYTHING*. TAKE NOTE OF ANY PACKET FOOD YOU EAT AS WELL, AS MANY SAUCES, SOUPS, CEREALS, MILK ALTERNATIVES (YOU NAME IT) HAVE ADDED SUGAR.

List all the foods/drinks that you LOVE and would be hard for you to give up.

Lisa's Musing

A little while back I went to Golden Door (now called Elysia Wellness Retreat). I wouldn't have said I ate a lot of sugar, but while I was there I had to cut it out completely. I remember playing games in my head during the first three days, like asking myself, "How far would you be prepared to run for one piece of cake?" I remember thinking, "at least 10km," even though I wasn't a runner at the time! However, when I left on day seven, the absolute last thing on my mind was sugar. From experience, it's painful at first, but as you get into it, your body is almost repulsed by it.

For some recipe inspo, search "sugar-free" on **womensweeklyfood.com.au,** and try the amazing ebooks from **iquitsugar.com/shop.**

FIND YOUR GREEN JUICE! THERE'S A REASON THAT GREEN JUICES ARE SO POPULAR. THEY'RE A GREAT WAY OF BOOSTING YOUR NUTRIENTS IN ONE HIT. TRY ADDING GREEN APPLE, CELERY OR SPINACH AND CREATE A COMBO YOU LOVE. SHARE YOUR RECIPE WITH US #COLLECTIVEHUB, OR POST IT IN OUR FACEBOOK GROUP: COLLECTIVE HUB CLUB.

Write down your recipe here:

_____

_____

_____

_____

_____

Lisa's Musing

I've been a green smoothie aficionado about 12 years. A girlfriend of mine introduced me to a book called *Green for Life*, and I was a convert from the start. I have one religiously every morning. I prefer it to juicing as smoothies maintain the fibre.

For recipes, visit **theblendergirl.com** or Google "Reese Witherspoon's morning smoothie". It's amazing.

EXPERIMENT. CHOOSE A HEALTH FOOD YOU'VE BEEN TOO AFRAID TO TRY AND MAKE A MEAL USING IT. IF YOU'RE NEW TO HEALTH FOODS, TRY CHIA SEEDS, HEMP SEEDS, QUINOA OR CHICKPEA FLOUR. ALREADY A HEALTH NUT? TRY KEFIR, AMARANTH OR SEAWEED.

What did you try? How did you use it? Did you like it?

_____

_____

_____

_____

_____

_____

Lisa's musing

Experimenting keeps it fresh, fun and interesting. Any food can feel a bit monotonous if you're just going through the motions. Explore nutritionists on Insta and look through their feeds and recipes to keep you encouraged.

Try **harrisfarm.com.au** or **goodness.com.au** for amazing health foods and recipes.

TREAT YOURSELF TO HEALTHY THREE-INGREDIENT PANCAKES! TAKE 1 BANANA, 2 EGGS AND A PINCH OF CINNAMON. MASH UNTIL SMOOTH. HEAT A NON-STICK FRYING PAN AND COOK ON BOTH SIDES UNTIL BROWN. TOP WITH BERRIES AND YOGHURT. COULDN'T BE EASIER!

Now add your personal touch to this recipe here:

_____

_____

_____

_____

_____

_____

Lisa's Musing

Oh, who doesn't love a pancake! My mother-in-law makes the best pancakes, but they are not the healthy version, so let's get into these! I can't wait to see what you create. Take a pic and share it with us #collectivehub or post it to our Facebook group (Collective Hub Club) along with your recipe, so we can all try it too!

Our favourite healthy pancake recipes from come from **thehealthychef.com** – so delicious!

LET'S GO COMBO CRAZY. IF YOU'RE RUNNING OUT OF HEALTHY EATING IDEAS TRY THESE: AVOCADO AND LOW-SUGAR JAM (YES, REALLY), MANGO AND PEANUT BUTTER ON TOAST, DARK CHOCOLATE (70 PER CENT OR HIGHER) AND A LITTLE CHILLI (GREAT FOR YOUR METABOLISM), VEGEMITE AND AVOCADO (ADD AN EGG TOO FOR EXTRA PROTEIN), PEAR AND ANY NUT BUTTER.

List your whacky combos and share them with us! #collectivehub
or post it in our Facebook group: Collective Hub Club.

_____

_____

_____

_____

_____

_____

Lisa's Musing

Okay, my editor Lucy contributed this day's idea, and I think she is slightly nuts for doing so. And at the same time I love her for it! Never say never. Here we go!

"Moderation. Small helpings. Sample a little bit of everything. These are the secrets of happiness and good health." – Julia Child

INVEST IN A GOOD HONEY: IT'S THE ONLY FOOD IN THE WORLD THAT NEVER SPOILS AND IT'S INCREDIBLY GOOD FOR YOU. YOU CAN EAT IT ON ITS OWN, HAVE IT IN TEA OR INCLUDE IT IN YOUR SMOOTHIES.

Fun fact: honey has been used in traditional healing for more than 5,000 years because of its antibacterial and wound-healing properties. List the ways you could add honey into your diet.

_____

_____

_____

_____

_____

_____

Lisa's Musing

I always have a good honey in my pantry. Any time I need a bit of a sweetener in pretty much anything, in goes some good honey. Be gone, sugars. Hello, honey!

For toast and tea try **melukaaustralia.com.au**, and for eating when you're sick or just on its own, **gohealthy.com.au**.

UPDATE YOUR MORNING VICE: TAKE THE SUGAR OUT OF YOUR COFFEE, DITCH TEA FOR UNCAFFEINATED ROOIBOS TEA, OR SWITCH TO COCONUT/OAT/MACADAMIA MILK. SEE WHAT OTHER DRINKS YOU COULD START YOUR DAY WITH.

What I usually have:

What I had this morning:

How it made me feel:

Lisa's Musing

I've been on the cow to soy to maca to oat milk bandwagon. Been there, tried them all. I've landed on oat for the moment and am very happy with my choice... until something better, newer, different comes along! Try different options until you find one that works for you; they are an acquired taste with different merits.

~~~~~~

"The secret of your future is hidden in your daily routine." – The Blissful Mind

LET'S GET ON TOP OF SNACKS. DID YOU KNOW WE CRAVE CRUNCHY FOODS WHEN WE WANT TO SNACK? IT'S AN EVOLUTIONARY THING. TODAY, SWAP OUT YOUR REGULARS WITH SOME HEALTHY ALTERNATIVES. PACK A SMALL CONTAINER IN YOUR BAG FOR SNACK ATTACKS.

Use the below columns to write your fave snacks on the left, and then what healthy alternatives you will swap them for on the right.

_____   _____

_____   _____

_____   _____

_____   _____

_____   _____

Lisa's musing

My one big weakness is chips. There, I said it. Cold chips, hot chips, crisps… Any member of the potato family. I am a sucker! But my 11-year-old niece recently introduced me to the 'crunch and sip' concept (parents, you know what I'm talking about). The way she talked about it and the way we packed those snacks, gave me a new appreciation for all things crunchy and healthy.

Get your snack inspo from celebrity PT Tiffiny Hall, with her book *Snack Power*. It's amazing!

MARCH 20

THINK ABOUT YOUR FAVOURITE TAKEAWAY MEAL. NOW, FIND A WAY TO MAKE A HEALTHY VERSION. TRY LETTUCE-WRAPPED NACHOS WITH YOGHURT, CAULIFLOWER-BASE PIZZA, GRILLED FISH AND SWEET POTATO CHIPS.

Write down some healthy versions of your favourites
that you can make in the weeks to come.

_____

_____

_____

_____

_____

Don't spend too long thinking about your favourite takeaway.
Just go there quickly in your brain, then do a mindset flip and think
about how you can do a healthy, fresh version of it. If you think about
it too long, before you know it you might have accidentally hit "order
now" on Uber Eats (whoops!).

For a bunch of ideas, log on to **healthyfoodguide.com.au**
and search for "homemade takeaways". Our favourite? Moroccan
pumpkin, chickpea and haloumi burgers – delicious!

START A HERB GARDEN, EVEN IF IT'S JUST ONE SMALL POT ON YOUR BALCONY, OR YOU COULD BUY A FEW BUNCHES OF HERBS FOR COOKING. FRESH HERBS CAN MAKE ALL THE DIFFERENCE TO A MEAL, AND THEY ADD EXTRA NUTRIENTS AS WELL.

Write down the herbs you regularly use in your cooking, and which ones you could grow yourself.

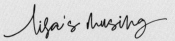

I just planted a herb and veggie garden at my mother-in-law's as a way to get my four-year-old niece excited about eating her veggies. We literally had a plot of soil about 1.5m x 0.5m, but we had so much fun planting it. Just seeing her get excited and starting to understand the food chain gave me so much joy. I grew up in the country and we grew a lot of our own food, so wherever I live in the city, I'm a fan of the urban balcony.

For advice, search "herbs" at **lovethegarden.com**.

PLAY WITH YOUR FOOD: DESIGN A MEAL TO EAT WITHOUT UTENSILS, WHETHER IT'S A TRADITIONAL INDIAN DINNER, NACHOS OR A FULL HESTON BLUMENTHAL EAT-OFF-THE-TABLE BONANZA.

Create a menu plan below with drinks, entrée, main and dessert in the space below. Share it with us #collectivehub, or post it in our Facebook group: Collective Hub Club.

_____

_____

_____

_____

_____

_____

_____

Lisa's musing

There is something super fun about this. I first encountered the experience in India about 15 years ago. Sometimes it's liberating to just dig in, let the Western tradition of utensils slide, and truly enjoy every mouthful, forget about the mess and live in the moment!

For inspiration, search "no-utensil recipes" on **food52.com**.

EAT THE RAINBOW TODAY. TICK OFF EVERY COLOUR OF THE RAINBOW IN THE FOODS YOU EAT. AIM FOR FRESH FRUIT AND VEGETABLES – AND REMEMBER, NO CHEATING WITH JELLY BEANS!

Choose a healthy food in each of the colours below, list them out and then eat them/tick them off throughout the day. We've added a few to help you.

Tomato   Orange   Lemon   Cucumber   Blueberry   Eggplant   Purple cabbage

Lisa's musing

See how we're making this fun, fun, fun? Hopefully each day you're starting to explore different ways of doing things, rather than just the same old, same old. I challenge you... how many colours can you get? Please send me a photo. I need all the inspo on this one! How pretty can you make it? Go for an edible work of art, please, and I promise I'll do the same.

"To keep the body in good health is a duty, otherwise we shall not be able to keep our mind strong and clear." – Buddha

MARCH 24

LET'S TALK SEEDS! FIND THEM IN THE HEALTH FOOD AISLE AND USE THEM AS EXTRA NUTRITIONAL CRUNCH ON YOUR TOAST OR IN SALADS, SMOOTHIES OR YOGHURT. THEY ARE FULL OF HEALTHY FATS AND ESSENTIAL FATTY ACIDS, FIBRE, MAGNESIUM, AND VITAMIN E - ALL THE GOOD STUFF.

Sprinkles to choose from: hemp seeds, chia seeds, crushed nuts, currants, seeds, even bee pollen all add extra nutrients to your meals. List out your meals for today and what 'healthy sprinkles' you can use on them.

_____

_____

_____

_____

_____

_____

Lisa's Musing

Trust me, this makes salads so much more enjoyable (and cereal for that matter). I have a pantry full of sprinkles and seeds. My fave go-to at the moment is vegan-friendly Pimp My Salad (**pimpmysaladonline.com**). They have loads of flavours and they feel so indulgent.

~~~~~~~~~~

Try online health stores **goodness.com.au** and **healthybeing.com.au**.

LET'S FOCUS ON GUT HEALTH TODAY - AIM FOR THREE SERVES OF GUT-FRIENDLY FOODS. TRY YOGHURT, MISO, KOMBUCHA, KIMCHI, SAUERKRAUT OR PICKLES. AND YOUR GUT REALLY LOVES LOTS OF FRESH WATER, OFTEN.

Write down the foods that make you bloated or don't agree with you.
Can you avoid those foods? What foods can you eat instead?

Personally I am loving sauerkraut and pickled veg at the moment.
I have a pretty funky gut so I'm all about trying anything that will
aid my digestion and stop that pesky bloating.

For ideas, look up health coach Lee Holmes via
superchargedfood.com, who specialises in gut health.

LET'S GO VEGAN FOR A DAY: SPEND TODAY EATING ONLY PLANT-BASED FOODS. HUMMUS CAN REPLACE CHEESE, AVOCADO CAN REPLACE CREAM OR BUTTER, EGGPLANT COULD WORK INSTEAD OF MEAT. TAKE A FEW OF YOUR FAVOURITE MEAT DINNERS AND WORK OUT HOW TO MAKE THEM MEAT-FREE, AND IF YOU'RE ALREADY MEAT-FREE, SWITCH UP SOME OF YOUR FAVOURITE VEGGIE PROTEINS.

Do you think this made a difference to how your body felt today? How? What could you continue to switch out in the future?

_____

_____

_____

_____

_____

Lisa's Musing

You can do this. I have spent several weeks at various raw food vegan communes around the world, and trust me days one to three are the hardest. By day four, you're chomping it down like you were always vegan. Check out Pachamama in Costa Rica (pachamama.com), where I have spent good chunks of time.

"Came from a plant, eat it; was made in a plant, don't." – Michael Pollan

TO REALLY ENJOY YOUR MEAL, TURN OFF THE TV AND YOUR DEVICES AND EAT AT YOUR DINING ROOM TABLE. YOU'LL FIND YOU EAT LESS, CHEW MORE AND HELP YOUR DIGESTION DO ITS THING. IF YOU CAN SHARE YOUR MEAL WITH SOMEONE, EVEN BETTER. REALLY WANT TO CHALLENGE YOURSELF? EAT IN THE DARK. WHILE IT MIGHT BE MESSY, YOUR TASTE BUDS GO INTO OVERDRIVE AND YOUR SENSE OF SMELL WILL BECOME INTENSE.

List some of the funniest conversation starters you can use:

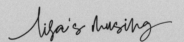

This is just a good habit to have. My partner and I found that we were getting a little lazy and eating in front of the TV most nights. We love food and good conversation, so we make it a habit to at least eat at the table, even if we Netflix and chill after.

Organise a blindfolded dinner party in your home with **chefin.com.au**.

CREATE A SIGNATURE HEALTHY PIZZA. CONSIDER USING A CAULIFLOWER BASE, THEN ADDING LOTS OF VEGGIES. INSTEAD OF CHEESE YOU CAN TRY HUMMUS, WHICH IS DELICIOUS WHEN COOKED! SHARE YOUR CREATION WITH US #COLLECTIVEHUB OR POST IT TO OUR FACEBOOK GROUP: COLLECTIVE HUB CLUB!

My healthy pizza recipe:

_____

_____

_____

_____

_____

_____

_____

Lisa's musing

This is so tasty, and it makes life a little more interesting. Hit on a good one. Share it with me! I'm always after different delicious combos!

～～～～～

Google "healthy pizzas" – there are so many online recipes for inspo.

WE KNOW THAT COMPLEX CARBS HAVE A PLACE IN A HEALTHY DIET, BUT JUST TO SEE HOW MUCH YOU RELY ON THEM, TODAY TRY REPLACING WHITE STUFF WITH GREEN STUFF: ZOODLES INSTEAD OF PASTA, LETTUCE INSTEAD OF BREAD, COCONUT WRAPS INSTEAD OF WHEAT ONES.

Write down your food swaps here:

_____   _____

_____   _____

_____   _____

_____   _____

_____   _____

Lisa's Musing

I've gotta say, bread and potatoes are my downfall. There is (almost) nothing better than hard crusty bread that is super soft in the middle. But then I think of my ever-growing waistline… Just remember your end game, whatever that might be, and it'll take you out of the instant gratification of the moment.

"For me, when I don't eat a ton of carbs, I have more energy. But I'll for sure have a piece of chocolate. I will mow through a bowl of guacamole. If I'm not going to have dessert, I'll have a martini." – Jessica Alba

LET'S GET CREATIVE WITH COCKTAILS! PICK THREE OF YOUR FAVE EVENING DRINKS AND REMAKE THEM TO BE HEALTHY AND ALCOHOL FREE. WHAT CAN YOU USE TO MAKE THEM DELICIOUS?

My old favourite:

_____

_____

_____

My new favourite:

_____

_____

_____

Lisa's musing

I'm the queen of making mocktails. I gave up drinking alcohol on 8 November 2004, and haven't touched a drop since. I only started drinking coffee for the first time in my life recently. So there was a big gap of about 12 years where I didn't drink tea, coffee or alcohol – so I had to get creative with delicious drink recipes. One of my faves is simply sparkling water with cucumber, lemon and mint. Delish!

We love **seedlipdrinks.com** for a non-alcoholic distilled spirits – a great alternative to gin.

PLAN YOUR DINNERS FOR THE NEXT WEEK. DO A SHOP TODAY TO ENSURE YOU HAVE EVERYTHING YOU NEED, AND PRE-COOK A FEW MEALS FOR THE FREEZER IF YOU HAVE TIME. HAVE A THINK ABOUT THE SNACKS YOU'LL EAT AS WELL. DO AS MUCH FOOD PREP AS YOU CAN TO GET SET UP.

Monday

Tuesday

Wednesday

Thursday

Friday

Lisa's Musing

Today I made a salad of baby spinach, broccolini, beans, snow peas, tomatoes, nuts and zucchini noodles. It'll last for three days in the fridge, so I can eat it over a few days adding some dressing and a protein (salmon, chicken) each day. Preparation is key to staying healthy.

"It is health that is real wealth and not pieces of gold and silver." – Mahatma Gandhi

april

BE MINDFUL

In our fast-paced, multi-faceted modern lives it can be difficult to stop and just… be. However, mindfulness has a huge amount of research behind it.

Spending even five minutes a day 'being present' can relieve stress, lower blood pressure, improve sleep, and help maintain a healthy gut. So this month we will be taking you on a journey to help you create time for meditation, mindfulness and self-reflection.

Unlike other months, during the next 30 days we'll be asking you to meditate every day, in addition to getting on board with our activities.

Why? Because we know that it will have such profound effects on you and your life that you'll fall in love with it, as we have done.

Plus, we'll explore how to be mindful in a world that never slows down. So, come on, let's take in all that silence…

APRIL 1

A BIG PART OF MINDFULNESS IS STILLNESS AND MEDITATION, SO THIS MONTH WE ASK YOU TO MEDITATE EVERY DAY. FIND A TIME THAT WORKS, SIT DOWN AND ENJOY THE QUIET. IF YOU'RE A NEWBIE, START WITH FIVE- OR 10-MINUTE GUIDED MEDITATIONS. IF YOU'RE A PRO TRY A DIFFERENT TECHNIQUE, OR CHALLENGE YOURSELF TO MEDITATE TWICE A DAY.

What came up for you today during meditation? Share your feelings below.

_____

_____

_____

_____

_____

_____

Lisa's Musing

I've been meditating for a loooong time. You'll learn more about my various meditation techniques throughout this chapter. Don't worry, when I first started meditation it drove me bonkers. I couldn't sit still. I couldn't quieten my mind. But over time, I found what worked for me – and you will too. Stick with it and just start somewhere.

Check out these apps: **Calm. Buddhify. Sattva. Insight Timer.**

TODAY, TAKE TIME TO WORK OUT YOUR PERFECT MORNING RITUAL. WHAT WOULD YOU LIKE TO DO AND ACHIEVE EACH MORNING? ROUTINES ARE THE KEY TO STARTING THE DAY RIGHT.

Use the below timeline to map out your perfect morning routine.

6am:

7am:

8am:

9am:

10am:

11am:

12pm:

Lisa's Musing

Here's the thing: I sleep eight to 10 hours every single night. And in an ideal world, I don't get up until 8am. But once I'm up and my rituals and routines kick in, I'm ON and unstoppable for the rest of the day.

"You'll never change your life until you change something you do daily. The secret of your success is found in your daily routine." – John C. Maxwell

---

APRIL 3

ARE YOU BREATHING? ARE THEY SHORT, SHARP BREATHS OR LONG
LUSCIOUS BREATHS? THREE TIMES TODAY, SIT STILL, CLEAR YOUR MIND
(IF YOU CAN!) AND BREATHE DEEPLY FIVE TIMES. EACH TIME YOU EXHALE,
IMAGINE YOU ARE RELEASING STRESS AND TENSION, MORE AND MORE
UNTIL YOU HAVE NONE LEFT. REPEAT BEFORE BED.

List the emotions you felt when you took
these deep breaths. Did you feel calmer?

_____

_____

_____

_____

_____

_____

Lisa's Musing

This is a really good habit to get into. Breath is everything. I'm a mouth
breather, so I have to consciously practice breathing even more.

The Headspace App has a free breathing tutorial
on its website that we love: **headspace.com**

APRIL 4

POSTURE AFFECTS OUR DIGESTION, OUR MUSCLES, OUR CONFIDENCE AND OUR BREATHING, SO TODAY SET YOURSELF SIX REMINDERS ON YOUR PHONE TO GO OFF DURING THE DAY. EACH TIME CHECK HOW YOU ARE SITTING OR STANDING AND CORRECT YOUR POSTURE.

What are some of the other things you'd like to focus on when it comes to your health and wellbeing?

_____

_____

_____

_____

_____

_____

My partner has had a standing desk ever since I've known him. It might be worth trying one out if you want to get your posture right.

For standing desks try **zenspacedesks.com.au** or **omnidesk.com.au**, and for posture support try the Upright Go – it's super easy and corrects posture almost instantly (**uprightpose.com**).

LISTEN BEFORE YOU EAT LUNCH TODAY. CLOSE YOUR EYES FOR A FEW MINUTES AND LISTEN TO THE SOUNDS OF WHAT'S HAPPENING AROUND YOU. FIND A SOUND AND FOCUS ON IT FOR 10 SECONDS, BLOCKING EVERYTHING ELSE OUT. MAKE THIS A HABIT AND YOU'LL FIND YOU START TO LOOK FORWARD TO TAKING A MOMENT TO FIND PEACE.

What sounds did you hear?

_____

_____

_____

_____

Now, they might not be pleasant sounds! I just did this in the moment of writing and I could hear a construction worker, a loud blowfly, the hum of our air conditioner, a car roaring past and, oh there it is, a bird happily tweeting. They might not be the sounds you want to hear, but it's such a great exercise to bring you into the present moment.

"Our character is basically a composite of our habits. Because they are consistent, often unconscious patterns, they constantly, daily, express our character." – Stephen Covey

APRIL 6

PRACTICE MINI PAUSES: FEEL THE DOOR HANDLE IN YOUR HAND, THE SOCKS ON YOUR FEET, OR LISTEN TO THE SOUND OF YOUR PARTNER/ CHILDREN/DOG CALLING FOR YOU BEFORE YOU ANSWER. TAKING MINI PAUSES TO APPRECIATE SENSATIONS CAN HELP GROUND YOU.

Did these mini pauses help you manage any stress today?
What mini pauses do you remember? Write some down here:

_____

_____

_____

_____

_____

_____

Lisa's Musing

This is the best thing. I am such a reactive person (it comes with the territory of people pleasing). But when I stop, breathe and pause before I react, a sense of calm washes over me. It stops the knee-jerk reaction and becomes a more conscious, proactive, thoughtful response.

"Be happy in the moment, that's enough. Each moment is all we need, not more." – Mother Teresa

EAT BY NUMBERS. STUDIES SHOW THAT MINDFUL EATING CAN HELP PEOPLE RECOGNISE HUNGER CUES AND MAKE HEALTHY AND NUTRITIOUS CHOICES - SO BEFORE YOU EAT TODAY, RATE YOUR HUNGER OUT OF 10, 10 BEING READY FOR A LARGE MEAL, ONE TO FOUR BEING MOST PROBABLY BORED, STRESSED OR TIRED RATHER THAN HUNGRY. HAVE A BIG GLASS OF COLD WATER AND WAIT 15 MINS. DRINKING WATER HELPS TO CURB THOSE 'HUNGER' THOUGHTS WHEN YOU DON'T REALLY NEED A SNACK.

Circle how hungry you are before you eat your meal! Then write down what you ate. Did rating your hunger affect what you had?

Breakfast	Lunch	Dinner	Snacks
1 2 3 4 5	1 2 3 4 5	1 2 3 4 5	1 2 3 4 5
6 7 8 9 10	6 7 8 9 10	6 7 8 9 10	6 7 8 9 10

_____   _____   _____   _____
_____   _____   _____   _____

Lisa's Musing

Those of us with addictive personalities will often reach for anything to fill the void – so, for me, this is a really mindful way of checking in before I reach.

"I love to eat everything and you pretty much can – a little piece of something fattening is not going to kill you. It's when you eat the whole box that it's going to kill you. If you can learn to not eat till your stomach feels full and gross, then you can pretty much control your life in that area." – Jennifer Lopez

APRIL 8

MIX UP YOUR ROUTINE: TAKE A DIFFERENT WAY TO WORK, DRIVE TILL YOU GET LOST OR PLACE A NEW COFFEE ORDER AND FOCUS ON THE DIFFERENCE. MIXING UP YOUR ROUTINE, EVEN JUST A LITTLE, IS LIKE TAKING A VACATION IN MINDFULNESS.

List five ways you mixed up your routine today. Did you like it, or did it make you feel uncomfortable?

Lisa's musing

This is a technique I first learned in 2004 when I gave up drinking. It is such a great exercise and I embrace doing something different, outside my comfort zone, every single day.

"Let today be the day you give up who you've been for who you can become." – Hal Elrod

APRIL 9

THE SIMPLE ACT OF HUGGING CAN LOWER STRESS AND RELEASE FEEL-GOOD HORMONES. TODAY WE CHALLENGE YOU TO HUG AS MANY PEOPLE, DOGS, CHILDREN, TREES AS YOU CAN. ASK PERMISSION FIRST, OF COURSE! BUT GET ON IN THERE AND MAKE SOMEONE SMILE. YOU'LL REAP THE BENEFITS TOO.

Make a list of everyone you hugged today!

_____

_____

_____

_____

_____

_____

Lisa's Musing

I am such a hugger! How tricky was lockdown when
we couldn't do it? I'll hug anyone, any time.

*"Sometimes when you don't know what
to say, a hug says enough."* – Anon

WATCH TV: IT DOESN'T SOUND LIKE A CHALLENGE, BUT TRY DOING IT WITHOUT ANOTHER DEVICE IN YOUR HAND. ONE WHOLE SHOW OR MOVIE. PUT YOUR PHONE ON SILENT, CLOSE YOUR LAPTOP AND TURN OFF YOUR IPAD.

What movie did you watch? Did you feel like checking your phone? Were you able to concentrate?

_____

_____

_____

_____

_____

_____

Lisa's Musing

My fave, most delicious show was *Younger* on Stan. Absolutely loved it. I love anything where you can get completely lost in the characters. *Downton Abbey* had a similar effect on me.

~~~~~~

Netflix documentaries we love to get lost in include: *Minimalism: A Documentary About the Important Things* (2016), *The Social Dilemma* (2020), *Fyre: The Greatest Party That Never Happened* (2019) and *David Attenborough: A Life on Our Planet* (2020).

PUT ASIDE AN HOUR TODAY TO ASSESS YOUR FINANCIAL SITUATION. HOW MUCH DO YOU PAY EACH MONTH ON NECESSITIES (RENT, BILLS, ETC) AND ROUGHLY HOW MUCH DO YOU SPEND PER DAY ON INCIDENTALS (COFFEE, ONLINE SHOPPING, ETC).

Now sketch out a savings plan, if you don't already have one. How much can you transfer each month into a savings account? What are your goals for that money? How long will you give yourself to reach each goal?

Lisa's Musing

If you want a way to navigate this (and make it all much easier), check out our *Know Your Numbers Journal* available at **collectivehub.com**. I know so many creatives who don't enjoy the money side of things, but, for me, the numbers are everything and nothing. That guide will help you map everything out.

Check out our the blog of our favourite financial coach Jane Walters for tips on how to be finance fit: **janekwalters.com/moneytips**.

WHILE YOU'RE IN TRANSIT TODAY, CLEAR YOUR MIND AND THINK ABOUT THE THINGS THAT MAKE YOU SMILE. THEN LINGER ON EACH ONE AND FEEL GRATITUDE FOR THEM.

List the five things that made you smile today

Here are mine for today: the sun on my face when I went for my morning walk, cuddles from my cavoodle Benny when I woke up, a call from my mum telling me she'd just finished her latest painting, my goofy partner doing a dance out of the shower, running on my treadmill and sounding like a crazy person (I run hard and it makes me laugh at the ridiculousness of the sounds I make).

"A smile is a curve that sets everything straight." – Phyllis Diller

@COLLECTIVEHUB #COLLECTIVEHUB

APRIL 13

SEEK OUT A VIEW TODAY. IT COULD BE YOUR FAVOURITE COAST OR PARK VIEW, IT MIGHT BE JUST THE VIEW FROM YOUR OFFICE, BUT TAKE A MOMENT TO REALLY LOOK AT IT. HOW FAR CAN YOU SEE? WHAT'S YOUR FAVOURITE PART? SHARE YOUR VIEW WITH US.

Try to sketch that view. Don't worry if you're not much of an artist. Just try to capture it in a different way.

Lisa's Musing

I'm grateful for the view from my home office; it only spans about four metres, but it's full of lush plants from floor to ceiling. It makes me happy as I write. And I also love the view from the cliffs of Bondi. At night looking from south to north it's like a tiny twinkling tinseltown of fairy lights. In the day, the horizon goes on forever. It makes me think life is infinite and so much bigger than me.

"I felt my lungs inflate with the onrush of scenery – air, mountains, trees, people. I thought, 'This is what it is to be happy'." – Sylvia Plath

LET GO OF MULTI-TASKING AND EMBRACE MONO-TASKING (YES, IT'S REALLY CALLED THAT!). FOCUS ON DOING AND COMPLETING ONE TASK AT A TIME TODAY. IT WILL BE A CHALLENGE, WE KNOW!

What is the one task you focussed on today. How did that make you feel? Did you find you were more productive? What challenges did you face?

_____

_____

_____

_____

_____

_____

Lisa's Musings

Oh gosh! I am so not the right person to write about this. I am the queen of multitasking. But I guess the reason I can do so much is that when I am working on one thing, I do it with precision focus. So, for a bit of fun, today's focus was this book. I pumped out heaps and it was challenging to keep inspiring myself as I wrote.

Jump onto **Medium.com** and pop in "the art of mono tasking". There are some great reads.

**CALL A FRIEND TODAY AND ASK THEM HOW THEY ARE FEELING.
REALLY LISTEN TO THE ANSWER. DON'T THINK ABOUT YOUR TO-DO LIST,
OR WORRY ABOUT WHAT ADVICE TO GIVE, JUST LET THEIR THOUGHTS
SIT WITH YOU AND LET THEM KNOW YOU ARE THERE FOR THEM.**

Write a list of 10 people you haven't really checked in with lately. Pick one
to call today and then circle back on the others by the end of the month.

1. _____   6. _____

2. _____   7. _____

3. _____   8. _____

4. _____   9. _____

5. _____   10. _____

Lisa's Musing

Sometimes I call someone and I'm really not present. I did it with my
mum the other day, and it was like I was going through the motions.
I felt terrible when I got off the call. So, I took my shoes off, grounded
myself, sat in nature, got present and called her back. I apologised for
not really being there 10 minutes before and owned my tardiness. And
do you know what? We had one of the best calls of my life.

*"I like to listen. I have learned a great deal from listening
carefully. Most people never listen."* – Ernest Hemingway

BEFORE BED TONIGHT, TAKE TIME TO CLEAN THE KITCHEN, PACK YOUR BAG AND LAY OUT YOUR CLOTHES FOR TOMORROW MORNING. THINK OF IT AS A TREAT FOR YOURSELF; WHEN YOU WAKE UP YOU CAN CONCENTRATE ON YOUR BREATHING RATHER THAN SNEAKERS VS HEELS.

Plan your morning here:

Lisa's Musing

My good friend Lorna Jane Clarkson taught me years ago the power of laying out a killer workout outfit the night before to a) get excited about it, and b) remove any excuses of not being able to find something in the morning. And my wonderful mother-in-law definitely reminds me about a clean kitchen. She is meticulous and I love her for it.

"Sow a thought, reap an action; sow an action, reap a habit; sow a habit, reap a character; sow a character, reap a destiny." – Stephen R. Covey

APRIL 17

SPEND THE MORNING OFF YOUR PHONE (YES, SOCIAL MEDIA AND EMAIL!). DEPENDING ON YOUR DAY AHEAD, THIS MIGHT BE BETWEEN WAKING UP AND YOUR 9AM MEETING, OR IT COULD BE UNTIL LUNCHTIME. TAKE NOTE OF YOUR ANXIETY LEVEL – IS IT REDUCED BY BEING OFFLINE?

Write down how if felt to be off your phone. Were you anxious, did you love it, or were you indifferent?

I've said it before and I'll say it again. I have a total love/hate relationship with social media. There's absolutely no doubt whatsoever that I feel so much better when I am off all technology. Unquestionably. So take some control back and don't let people pull at you constantly. And breathe.

The SPACE app can break phone addiction and help you stay focused. See **findyourphonelifebalance.com**.

MEDITATION CHECK-IN: HOW ARE YOU GOING? HAVE YOU LET IT SLIDE OR ARE YOU STILL MEDITATING EVERY DAY? IF YOU'VE BEEN DOING IT FOR FIVE MINUTES, TRY 10, OR TRY WITHOUT USING A GUIDED MEDITATION. IT'S ALL ABOUT WHAT WORKS FOR YOU.

Write down five things you love about meditation:

Lisa's musing

Don't worry, the trick is – like most things – consistency. I know when I stop for a while or let my habit slide (trust me, it happens), it's so much harder to get back into it. So practice makes perfect, even if you just do a few minutes a day.

Need a little guidance? Try **soulalive.com.au** for weekly guided meditations via Instagram.

**LIGHT YOUR FAVOURITE CANDLE, MAKE A WARM DRINK, AND SIT
AND WATCH THE FLAME FLICKER AND FLARE FOR FIVE MINUTES.
IF YOUR MIND WANDERS, GENTLY BRING IT BACK TO THE FLAME.**

Did any thoughts come up while you were
watching the flame? List them below.

Lisa's musing

Such an easy and delicious meditation. I often do
this in the bath. Double dose of goodness.

～～～～～

Ecoya has beautiful candles and diffusers.

FOCUS ON BREATHING AGAIN TODAY. TAKE FIVE LONG BREATHS IN, AND FIVE OUT, THEN REDUCE THE NUMBER EACH TIME. SO FOUR BREATHS, THEN THREE AND SO ON. THIS METHOD CAN HELP REDUCE STRESS AND HELP YOU FOCUS ON ONE ACTION, ONE FEELING.

What other ways can you reduce the stress in your life? List them below:

_____

_____

_____

_____

_____

_____

Lisa's Musing

You can also try circular breathing doing this: put one finger over one nostril as you breathe in. Then, as you breathe out, change the finger to the other side. Also, count to the same number on the in breath and the out breath.

A simple app to help with this is **breathball.com**

APRIL 21

LOOK INWARDS TODAY. FIND A QUIET SPOT AND, FOR 10-15 MINUTES, ASK YOURSELF "HOW DO I FEEL?" THEN TAKE YOURSELF THROUGH THE EMOTIONS IN YOUR HEAD. IF YOU FEEL HAPPY, DISSATISFIED, CHALLENGED, NEGATIVE, SAD, ASK YOURSELF WHY, AND REALLY EXPLORE THE REASONS BEHIND YOUR EMOTIONS.

Write down honestly how you feel in this present moment:

_____

_____

_____

_____

_____

_____

It's really important to feel things. The good. The bad. All of it. Feel it deeply. Don't get busy and try to ignore it. Work out why you are feeling it, and then make peace with it. We all have off days and great days. It's about learning to manage our triggers and emotions, and harnessing the tools to help us through them.

A great book to read on this topic is *The Happiness Hypothesis* by psychologist Jonathan Haidt.

APRIL 22

COOKING HAS BEEN LINKED TO MEDITATION AS IT ALLOWS THE MIND TO FOCUS ON ONE THING. SO PLAN TO COOK SOMETHING SPECIAL TONIGHT – IT DOESN'T HAVE TO BE RESTAURANT QUALITY AND IT'S FINE IT IT'S JUST FOR YOU, BUT CHOOSE A RECIPE YOU HAVEN'T DONE BEFORE AND GIVE YOURSELF THE TIME TO ENJOY PULLING IT ALL TOGETHER. USE THE GOOD PLATES!

Record the recipe that you cooked so you can refer back to it.

_____

_____

_____

_____

_____

_____

Lisa's Musing

Cooking is one of my greatest loves. For me it's another creative outlet. I love exploring different dishes. I love the art of it, and the final presentation. Have fun with it.

"Cooking is like love. It should be entered into with abandon or not at all." – Harriet Van Horne

@COLLECTIVEHUB #COLLECTIVEHUB

WORK ON YOUR BALANCE TODAY – IT ENGAGES YOUR CORE AND ALSO YOUR MINDFUL MIND. SOME WAYS TO DO THIS ARE SURFING, STAND-UP PADDLEBOARDING, YOGA POSES, HANDSTANDS, OR WALKING ALONG BALANCE BARS AT PARK GYMS.

Try standing on one leg three times today and record how long you can stand tall without wobbling or falling over.

First attempt
How long did you last?

Second attempt
How long did you last?

Third attempt
How long did you last?

Lisa's Musing

Fun fact: my balance is terrible! I literally run into door frames as I get off-kilter, and when I do Pilates on the reformer machines, I'm the only one in the class who has to hold on when doing standing leg exercises. It's okay to not be perfect at something. Just be aware of it and keep working on it. I'm getting better and I do it all with gusto and full force. So don't be too hard on yourself.

"Balancing in yoga and life is a reflection of our inner state." – Shiva Rea

VISIT AN ART GALLERY, MUSEUM, OR BOOKSTORE AND FOCUS ON ONE OR TWO OBJECTS. WHAT ARE THEY MADE OF, HOW WOULD THEY FEEL TO TOUCH, ARE THEY ANGULAR OR DO THEY HAVE SHARP EDGES? TURN OFF YOUR PHONE AND ENJOY THE QUIET BREAK FROM THE WORLD.

Sketch your favourite object from today:

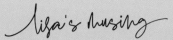

Some days I take myself on a walking tour of museums and galleries, especially if I'm travelling, but also sometimes in my own city. There are wonderful little galleries everywhere. Just give it a Google.

The National Gallery of Victoria has free virtual tours on its website: **ngv.vic.gov.au/virtual-tours**.

TO HELP YOU SLEEP AND CURB ANY STRESS YOU MIGHT HAVE, CARVE OUT SOME 'WORRY TIME' THIS AFTERNOON WHERE YOU WRITE DOWN ALL THE THINGS YOU ARE CONCERNED ABOUT. THE IDEA BEHIND THIS IS THAT BY THE TIME YOU GET TO BED, YOU WON'T BE THINKING ABOUT THEM.

List your concerns and any ways you think you can overcome them below.

_____

_____

_____

_____

_____

Lisa's Musing

I have a wonderful little trick that I taught myself to deal with my worries. In your mind's eye, go to the worst-case scenario. Then reverse engineer it to the current moment. Along the way, think about who could support you. Once you do this and then take some action (send an email, make a phone call, share your worry with someone capable of helping) it is so much less overwhelming.

Ask yourself, will it matter 10 minutes from now?
Will it matter 10 months from now? Will it matter 10 years
from now? Perspective is a wonderful thing.

PRACTICE THE ART OF BEING PRESENT. AS YOU GO ABOUT YOUR DAY, TRY TO FOCUS ON WHAT IS HAPPENING RIGHT NOW; DON'T START THINKING ABOUT YOUR TO-DO LIST, OR YOUR BIG DAY TOMORROW, JUST KEEP PULLING YOUR MIND BACK TO THE TASK AT HAND.

List all the worries and concerns that came up during this exercise:

Lisa's musing

We only have now. There is no real point in thinking about yesterday. It has already gone. Bring yourself into the now.

"Wherever you are, be there totally." – Eckhart Tolle

FOR A SLOW, MINDFUL MOVEMENT, TRY YIN YOGA TODAY. IT INVOLVES ONLY A FEW POSES IN EACH CLASS, AND YOU HOLD THE POSES FOR MUCH LONGER THAN USUAL. IT'S A WORKOUT FOR YOUR MIND AND YOUR BODY.

List what you enjoyed and what you found challenging about this class:

_____

_____

_____

_____

_____

Lisa's Musing

When I first did a yin yoga class, many moons ago, and didn't move off the floor, I thought… boring. But it was (and is) exactly what I needed. I tend to go for high energy, heart pumping, adrenaline-fuelled exercises. What I find I need most is counterintuitive to that: slow, restorative. I now absolutely love yin yoga and my partner and I go to a Sunday night class together whenever we're in Sydney.

Check out the YouTube channel, Allie - The Journey Junkie, for some great yin yoga online classes.

APRIL 28

**MINDFUL MUSIC: LISTENING TO MUSIC AFFECTS OUR STRESS LEVEL,
MOOD, AND EVEN OUR HEARTBEAT. SPEND TODAY FINDING THE PERFECT
TRACKS TO LISTEN TO WHEN YOU ARE HAPPY, SAD, ANGRY, TIRED. MAKE
A FEW PLAYLISTS SO THE NEXT TIME YOU WANT TO CHANGE YOUR MOOD,
OR EMBRACE YOUR MOOD, YOUR PLAYLISTS ARE WAITING FOR YOU.**

Make a list of three songs for each column below:

Happy	Sad	Calm	Excited
1.	1.	1.	1.
2.	2.	2.	2.
3.	3.	3.	3.

Lisa's Musing

One of the many meditations I've done is called a 'burn meditation'.
It can go for up to six hours. The music is curated from soft, heart-
wrenching music that can have me in puddles of tears. Then the tempo
changes and I'll be dancing my arse off to house tribal beats, pumping
anger through my veins. This is not a meditation for the faint-hearted,
but it has certainly taught me that surrendering to music can have
a profound impact on me. Very cathartic.

For meditation music, check out the
YouTube channel Music for Body and Spirit.

APRIL 29

GIVE YOURSELF A MASSAGE OR SPLURGE AND VISIT A SPA. TRY TO CLEAR YOUR MIND AND FOCUS ONLY ON YOUR MUSCLES AND THE WAY THEY FEEL. FOLLOW THE HANDS ON YOUR BACK WITH YOUR MIND AND NOTE HOW DIFFERENT PARTS OF YOUR BACK AND NECK FEEL.

Write down how you feel before your massage, then return to this page and write down how you feel afterwards:

_____

_____

_____

_____

_____

Lisa's Musing

I've been having a massage at least once a week for years. The funniest experience I ever had was in Marrakesh in Morocco, where I found myself in a traditional Turkish Bath… Hysterical. I've never laughed so hard. What I will say is get really clear on what you do and don't like in a massage. For example, I can't stand when they slop a wet towel all over you at the end to wipe off the oil. I find it gross. Work out what works for you and be upfront about what you want.

~~~

Find a mobile masseuse who'll come to your house at **getblys.com.au**.

APRIL 30

START LISTENING TO A MINDFUL PODCAST OR DOWNLOAD A MINDFUL APP SO YOU CAN CONTINUE TO IMPROVE YOUR MINDFUL SKILLS.

List some of your favourite mindful podcasts below and share them with us #collectivehub or post a pic to our Facebook group (Collective Hub Club), so we can all check them out. We love a good poddy recommendation!

_____

_____

_____

_____

_____

Lisa's Musing

You did it. Another month! I'm so proud of you. Take a deep breath. Now let's get ready for another beautiful, bold connected month of discovery and learning. It's time to start anew. And just know I am right here with you going along day by day, exercise by exercise. So don't ever feel alone or like you're in this by yourself.

Good podcasts to listen to are: *Mindful in Minutes,*
Meditation Minis, The Mindful Minute.

What did you love about this month and what have you learned?

_____

_____

_____

_____

_____

_____

_____

_____

_____

_____

_____

_____

_____

_____

may

SACRED PLACES

A sacred space is an area in your home that is meaningful, full of calm feelings and dedicated entirely to you.

This month is all about finding those sacred spaces in our lives and in our homes that you can retreat to. Why? Well, when we feel safe and protected in our space, our 'flight or fight' reflex is switched off. We not only connect better to our goals and to ourselves, but also to those around us.

So, each day this month we'll bring you closer to creating that personal space just for you, with a set-up that will welcome and inspire, and a ritual or routine that will centre you.

This month is all about giving you the chance to really ground yourself in the world and claim a piece of it as your own.

WHAT DO YOU VALUE IN YOUR SURROUNDINGS? FOR ME, IT'S FRESH AIR, NATURAL LIGHT, LIVE PLANTS, LAUGHTER AND A COMFY COUCH.

Write down 10 things you value in your surroundings

1. _____
2. _____
3. _____
4. _____
5. _____

6. _____
7. _____
8. _____
9. _____
10. _____

Lisa's Musing

This section is about mindfully, consciously, purposefully spending each day feeling into and getting really clear about what surroundings are most supportive to you. It's a wonderful exercise to take yourself through, and, let's face it, how often in life do we take time to really consciously create spaces and surroundings that support us? This month, that is exactly what we are doing. Let's think of it as a 'space renovation'. It's about decluttering, and making small or large changes to support you in all the spaces you frequent.

"Your sacred space is where you can find yourself over and over again."
– Joseph Campbell

TAKE YOUR MIND TO PLACES THAT YOU FEEL SAFE, LOVED, NURTURED. THIS SIMPLE EXERCISE WILL GROUND YOU AND HELP CREATE A SENSE OF CALM AND PEACE IN YOUR DAY TODAY.

List 12 places you love, and spend a minute on each one thinking about why it's so special to you.

1. _____

2. _____

3. _____

4. _____

5. _____

6. _____

7. _____

8. _____

9. _____

10. _____

11. _____

12. _____

Lisa's Musing

There is so much coming at us every single day from our external environment that I believe it's important to control the things we can. And one of those things is our spaces. Our sacred spaces.

~~~~~~~~

Find articles about happiness and improving mental health at **happify.com**.

TIME TO GET BRAVE. THINK ABOUT WHAT TRIGGERS YOU: WHEN YOU DON'T FEEL GREAT, WHAT DO YOU AVOID (DARK, COLD, DAMP SPACES, INTENSE MUSIC, LOUD NOISES) AND WHAT DO YOU CRAVE (LIGHTNESS, BRIGHTNESS, AIR, LIVE PLANTS, CALMING FRIENDS).

Use the space below to write your triggers, and then list what you'd like to replace them with.

_____

_____

_____

_____

_____

_____

Lisa's musing

To live our best life, it's important that our surroundings support us. I couldn't care less about material possessions. It's not how big your home is or what you can afford (my happiest homes have been the smallest!), but I do care, deeply, about the spaces I create for myself.

Beyond Blue (**beyondblue.org.au**) has so many amazing resources to help with depression and feelings of anxiousness.

SACRED Q&A #1
WHERE DO YOU FEEL MOST MOTIVATED?

Write a description of it or draw it, and list three characteristics of that space:

Liza's musing

If you have a traditional profession, such as being an accountant or a lawyer, and you have beige boardrooms with mahogany tables – but this doesn't make you feel alive or motivated, instead it makes you feel rather stifled, then you can't do your best work.

Best-selling author James Clear has some great articles about motivation: **jamesclear.com/motivation**.

SACRED Q&A #2
WHERE DO YOU FEEL THE HAPPIEST?

Write a description of it or draw it, and list three characteristics of that space:

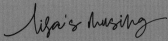

Forget other people's or society's expectations of what happiness means. Instead, ask yourself: when are you most happy, what makes you truly feel alive, what brings you joy, what brings a smile to your face? More often than not, for me, it's the really simple things. Walks in nature with my partner and Benny, my dog. Calls with my mum. Exercising. Having a massage. I love, love, love work and that makes me happy, but that's more the big fist-pumping stuff.

"I refuse to accept other people's ideas of happiness for me.
As if there's a one-size-fits-all standard for happiness." – Kanye West

SACRED Q&A #3
WHERE DO YOU FEEL MOST RELAXED?

Write a description of it or draw it, and list three characteristics of that space:

Lisa's Musing

To me, my home has absolutely got to be a sacred, nurturing safe space. Then whatever the world brings at me, I always know I can curl up in my little sanctuary. This is one of the reasons this chapter is so important to me, personally. We all need somewhere we can retreat to and feel totally relaxed.

Find stress-busting tips and relaxation techniques at **helpguide.org**.

SACRED Q&A #4
NAME ALL THE PLACES THAT INSPIRE YOU.

It could be an art gallery, a city (New York, Paris), a friend's house
or the botanic gardens. Where do you feel inspiration hit you?

Think outside the box here. I am inspired by all sorts of places.
Byron Bay for the creativity and little hubs, and also the incredible
nature, both the hinterland and the beaches. But I also find small
stores and lots of books inspiring. When you are open to seeing it,
there is truly inspiration everywhere.

Search 'why inspiration matters' for a great article
in the *Harvard Business Review* (**hbr.org**).

MEMORY LANE: WHAT WERE YOUR FAVOURITE SPACES AND PLACES TO GO WHEN YOU WERE A CHILD? THINK ABOUT WHY YOU LOVED THEM.

Write down what they were like and how they made you feel.

_____

_____

_____

_____

_____

_____

Liza's musing

At about age 6 I loved going to the creek and making mud pies. It brought hours of creative joy. I grew up on a 4,500 acre property and so we were always outside. I loved playing with my many animals – Jeremy the lamb, Sammy the dog, George the cockatoo. You name it, I had it! I was forever rescuing animals and I loved every minute.

To find out the importance of this, search 'playtime for adults' on **abc.net.au**.

LET'S GET GRANULAR. WITHIN YOUR HOME, WHICH AREAS ARE MOST IMPORTANT TO YOU AND WHY?

Draw a layout of your home and mark up the areas you feel most comfortable, and the areas you avoid.

Lisa's musing

You know after a frenetic day where the world has gone slightly mad, you've been pulled in a zillion directions and you're feeling a little overwhelmed and discombobulated? All you want is to come home to somewhere safe, secure, constant, consistent, and nurturing.

We love the interior design articles from **homebeautiful.com.au**.

MAY 10

SPEND 15 TO 20 MINUTES FOLLOWING INSTAGRAM ACCOUNTS OR HASHTAGS THAT ARE BIG ON SPACE CREATION THAT FITS YOUR AESTHETIC.

Write eight things you loved from these accounts today:

1. _____

2. _____

3. _____

4. _____

5. _____

6. _____

7. _____

8. _____

Just don't go down too much of a rabbit hole and too often.
I find once I start exploring, it can lead me on a never-ending
thread. Give yourself a time limit.

〜〜〜〜

Some thought starters: @yellowtrace,
@jessicavwalsh, @jonathanadler.

**NOW TO FOCUS ON PODCASTS! CHOOSE THREE PODCASTS
TO SUBSCRIBE TO THAT ARE ABOUT INTERIOR DESIGN, MINIMALIST
OR SACRED SPACES, OR THAT ARE INSPIRATIONAL.**

Get committed and list times and spaces where you'll listen them this week.

_____

_____

_____

_____

_____

_____

_____

Lisa's musing

I started listening to podcasts on my morning walks and on long
drives a few years ago. I really love them. The confusion for me often
comes in the overwhelm of choice. Ask your friends what they listen
to and then just try a bunch out according to your tastes.

Some to consider: *The Wellness Design Podcast,*
The Great Indoors, The Minimalists Podcast.

MAY 12

**OKAY, TIME TO GET CRAFTY. USE THIS PAGE AS
A MINI VISION BOARD FOR YOUR SACRED SPACES.**

Add things like colours, smells, textures, features, images of
furniture that inspires you and people who motivate you.

"Sacred spaces can be created in any environment."
– Christy Turlington

**CHOOSE ONE AREA OF YOUR HOME TO MAKE OVER.
USE THIS PAGE TO PLAN WHAT YOU NEED.**

What would you like to do, and how would you like this area to make you feel? It could be as simple as your desk or as complex as a bedroom. What are the five things you need to do to make that space more sacred?

1. _____

2. _____

3. _____

4. _____

5. _____

lisa's musing

Remember this doesn't have to be costly. Some of the most creative spaces I have conjured up have been using $3 Besser blocks from Bunnings and affordable wall hangings from dollar shops. Get thrifty and creative!

Watch *The Home Edit* on Netflix and get inspired. It's my current obsession.

MAY 14

TAKE TIME TODAY TO CLEAN OUT YOUR HANDBAG OR BACKPACK. SHAKE OUT ALL THE CRUMBS, GO THROUGH ALL THE OLD RECEIPTS AND CREATE A SPACE THAT WORKS FOR YOU. IF YOU DON'T USE A HANDBAG, CLEAN OUT YOUR CAR, MAKING SURE YOU HAVE EVERYTHING YOU NEED IN THERE.

Write down all the things you **need** in the space you're cleaning below.

_____

_____

_____

_____

_____

_____

Messy space: messy mind. That's certainly true for me. I can tell when things start getting messy and disorganised, that everything is becoming a bit unstuck. Your car, just like your home, office or wherever else, should be a reflection of your mind and personality. It should reflect the feelings you want when getting from A to B.

For beautiful, multi-purpose handbags with room for gym gear and a laptop, see **sparrodesigns.com.**

ON THE GO: IF YOU'RE TRAVELLING FOR WORK OR ON HOLIDAY, YOU CAN STILL MAKE A SPACE FEEL LIKE HOME WITH A FEW SIMPLE ADDITIONS.

Write down the things that you can use in your home that will remind you of home when you're on the go. Think about a particular candle or scent, the music you like to listen to, books you love, or even a small blanket or special pillowcase.

Lisa's Musing

When you travel a lot for work, you don't know which side is up! I like to take a few special things with me, like a teacup and a candle. Simple home comforts that ground you when you're anything but grounded.

"Each place is the right place – the place where I now am can be a sacred space." – Ravi Ravindra

MAY 16

TAKE THE TIME TODAY TO APPRECIATE PUBLIC SPACES. TRY TO VISIT SOMEWHERE OTHERS SEE AS SACRED. THIS COULD BE A MONUMENT, AN ART GALLERY, A SPECIAL BUILDING, A PLACE OF WORSHIP OR A GARDEN.

Write down all the feelings you have, the details you notice and the thoughts that appear in your mind as you appreciate the space.

Lisa's musing

Don't forget… open minds see inspiration everywhere.
Even in the most unexpected of places.

"'Sacred space' is another way of saying 'with intention'." – S. Kelley Harrell

MAY 17

TIME TO CREATE YOUR OWN SACRED SPACE. DESIGNATE AN AREA OR ROOM IN YOUR HOME, ADD CUSHIONS, LOOK AT THE LIGHTING (NATURAL LIGHT IS BEST), THE SCENTS, AND MAKE SURE THERE'S A SPACE WHERE YOU CAN SIT AND REFLECT. KEEP IT SIMPLE AND TRY TO HAVE IT OUT OF THE WAY OF THE BUSIEST PARTS OF YOUR HOME SO YOU CAN EMBRACE QUIETNESS.

Write your ideas and a plan below:

_____

_____

_____

_____

_____

_____

Lisa's Musing

I use Pinterest and Instagram for inspiration. Slowly but surely I'll build up something simple and to my liking. And I'll change it up every six to 12 months to keep it fresh. Some beautiful candles, rugs and cushions are a super easy start.

Want to do this digitally? Create a floorplan for your scared space using the magicplan app.

CREATE YOUR ALTAR: CHOOSE SOME PERSONAL ITEMS THAT MEAN SOMETHING TO YOU, AND CREATE A DISPLAY ON A TABLE IN YOUR SACRED SPACE. A SPOT YOU CAN VISIT, TIME AFTER TIME, AND ENJOY THE OBJECTS ALL OVER AGAIN.

Write down on this page what objects you chose and why. Revisit this page often, and if the objects have lost their meaning, replace them.

_____   _____

_____   _____

_____   _____

_____   _____

Lisa's Musing

I have a few things that are meaningful to me. One is a big framed artwork I had made, which is of an illustrated world map, and on it all the places my partner and I have been that meant something to us. On there I have added lots of little sayings, quotes and loads of photos of all the good times, and little stubs of things that meant something to us. I also have a candle. A dried flower. Some photos. A necklace I got at an ashram in India. Objects and reminders that ground and calm you, I find work well.

For beautiful one-of-a-kind objects to fill your space, see **australiandesigncentre.com**.

CREATE A ROUTINE FOR YOUR SACRED SPACE; A SIMPLE SET OF THINGS YOU'LL DO EACH TIME YOU TAKE THE TIME TO ENJOY YOUR SPACE. THIS COULD BE LIGHTING THE CANDLE, TURNING OFF YOUR PHONE, DEEP BREATHS AND MEDITATING.

Create an intention for the next time you visit your space:

_____

_____

_____

_____

_____

_____

_____

_____

Lisa's musing

I find my sacred space is symbolic as much as anything else. It just reminds me that I have somewhere to sit quietly and go inside myself. A space just for me. Somewhere I can sit and meditate.

We love the Relaxing Room Spray from **buckleyandphillips.com.au**.

LET'S EXPLORE OUR SENSE OF SMELL. THE SCENTS WE SURROUND OURSELVES WITH CAN BRING CALMNESS AND HELP US FEEL TRANQUIL, AND THEY CAN ALSO HELP US SLEEP. TODAY, EXPLORE THE SCENTS YOU WOULD LIKE TO BE THE HERO OF YOUR SACRED SPACE. THESE COULD BE CANDLES, ESSENTIAL OILS, SOY MELTS, PERFUMES OR FRESH FLOWERS.

Once you have found your favourite, make a list the kinds of smells in that scent. Is it woody, floral, sweet, fresh? This is a great exercise in mindfulness.

Lisa's musing

Smell is such an interesting sense. Scents are such distinctive markers in time for so many things. So try to recall smells you were surrounded by during happy, joyous times. I love the smell of mint, because when I was little I had mint plants growing outside my bedroom planted by my adoring grandmother. I also love the smell of rain on the earth, because it reminds me of galloping through paddocks and a complete sense of freedom growing up. The salt of the ocean (summer holidays)... I could go on and on.

Natural perfumes that we love include: **melisperfumery.com, kyndscent.com.au** and **aromantik.com.au.**

MEDITATE FOR 10 MINUTES IN YOUR SACRED SPACE TODAY. DOES THE SPACE MAKE YOU FEEL COMFORTABLE? IS IT MISSING SOMETHING?

Write down how you feel after your meditation, then note three things you love about your sacred space.

_____

_____

_____

_____

1. _____

2. _____

3. _____

Lisa's musing

This almost makes me laugh. Why? It's really easy for me to pull myself out of a meditation by thinking that an external factor is lacking… Maybe I'm just not letting myself go deep. In any case, a special place definitely helps until we get the gist of it. So create away.

For an online guided meditation, check out **centredmeditation.com.au**.

SOMETIMES THE SACRED SPACES WE SEEK CAN ONLY BE REACHED IN THE MIND. SO, TODAY, PULL TOGETHER A SACRED SPACES PLAYLIST THAT YOU CAN LISTEN TO IN YOUR SACRED SPACE, BUT ALSO ON HEADPHONES, IN TRANSIT, IN YOUR CAR. ANYWHERE YOU NEED TO HEAR IT.

Write down eight songs that make you feel safe, loved and inspired.

1. _____

2. _____

3. _____

4. _____

5. _____

6. _____

7. _____

8. _____

Lisa's musing

This is a way to ground yourself and feel safe wherever you are, whenever you want. I regularly meditate in the most unlikely of places. It's a really good habit to form and get comfortable with.

The noise-cancelling headphones from **bose.com.au** are amazing for cutting out outside noises.

FIND YOUR INSPIRATION. CHOOSE TWO TO THREE BOOKS FOR YOUR SCARED SPACE THAT YOU CAN DIP INTO AND ENJOY ON A DAILY BASIS. THESE COULD BE INSPIRING BIOGRAPHIES, MEMOIRS, OR SELF-HELP AND MOTIVATIONAL BOOKS. ANYTHING FROM WHICH YOU CAN GAIN WISDOM AND ENERGY.

What has been the most influential book in your life?

What is a lesson you learned from it?

What is one book you would like every person you know to read?

If you're anything like me, you'll love curling up and flicking through a few pages (or chapters!) of your fave book.

Some great reads to check out: *Man's Search for Meaning* by Viktor Frankl. *The Wisdom of Sundays* by Oprah Winfrey. *Daily Mantras to Ignite Your Purpose* by yours truly.

BRING IN NATURE: HELP CLEAN THE AIR IN YOUR SPACE BY INCLUDING PLANTS, OR DECORATE IT WITH FRESH FLOWERS OR A WATER FEATURE TO BRING IN THE ELEMENTS. MAKE SURE THE PLANT IS EASY TO CARE FOR, SUCH AS A PEACE LILY, WHICH ALSO HELPS TO DETOX THE AIR AROUND YOU.

Some more hard-to-kill plants are: aloe vera, money tree, pothos, ZZ plant, snake plant, prayer plant. Write down which rooms need a new plant in your home, and which plant suits that spot:

_____

_____

_____

_____

_____

_____

_____

Lisa's Musing

I *love* plants but they are expensive, so I've learned to propagate – and now have more than 100 plants in my home!

Inspo alert: we love **@helloplantlady** on Instagram.

MAY 25

**SET YOUR INTENTIONS: TAKE A MOMENT TO MAKE A COMMITMENT
TO YOUR SACRED SPACE. WHAT IS YOUR INTENTION WHEN IT COMES
TO THIS SPACE AND THIS TIME THAT YOU SET ASIDE?**

Write your intentions, making the most important ones large, and the less
important ones small. This page will help you prioritise your thoughts.

Intentions are a wonderful way to commit something
to paper and keep yourself accountable.

To help with setting intentions, try **chopra.com/app**.

THE POWER OF WORDS: SPEND SOME TIME TODAY GATHERING QUOTES, MANTRAS AND PRAYERS THAT RESONATE WITH YOU.

Write down as many as you can below, then choose two to five to write on paper and display in your scared space. Get creative with them and make them look beautiful and inspirational!

Lisa's Musing

Well, say no more: I love words. I love mantras. I love positive quotes. I love anything inspiring and uplifting. Words are powerful.

Our *Affirmations To Guide Your Journey* quote cards are perfect for this! Get yours here: **shop.collectivehub.com**.

EACH TIME YOU COME INTO THE SPACE, FOCUS ON SELF-CARE. THIS COULD BE A USING A FRAGRANT HAND CREAM, A FACE MIST, PERHAPS A BODY OIL. CHOOSE ONE THAT IS NON-TOXIC AND HAS A SCENT THAT IS CALMING.

Take a moment to write down the ways you love to do self care – do you like baths, manicures, facials, reading?

_____

_____

_____

_____

_____

_____

Lisa's Musing

Are you starting to feel comfortable in this space? Does it feel like you? Does it feel like home? Does it feel nurturing? I truly hope you're starting to feel all the feels.

"*We have to care about our bodies and what we put in them. Women have to take the time to focus on our mental health – take time for self, for the spiritual, without feeling guilty or selfish. The world will see you the way you see you, and treat you the way you treat yourself.*" – Beyoncé

CHOOSE A BREATHING TECHNIQUE TO USE IN YOUR SACRED SPACE THAT HELPS YOU FEEL CENTRED AND CALM.

Take a moment to write down the answer to this question:
How do you really feel right now?

_____

_____

_____

_____

_____

_____

Lisa's musing

The power of breath. So simple. And something I personally have to remind myself to work on consciously, every single day. When I'm doing a hard training session and I connect with my breath, suddenly it becomes so much easier. When I have a painful procedure at the beautician (Fraxel, anyone?) if I focus and breathe through it, the pain is so much less. When I'm meditating and doing yoga, breath is everything. Connect with it.

Some breathing apps to try are: MindShift CBT, Zenfie, Breath Ball.

TIME TO CLEAN YOUR SPACE. IT NEEDS REGULAR CLEANING, NOT ONLY FOR THE FENG SHUI BUT ALSO TO MAKE SURE IT'S TIDY, WITHOUT CLUTTER, EACH TIME YOU USE IT. TRY TO LEAVE YOUR SHOES OUT OF YOUR SPACE AS WELL, AND TRY TO USE NON-TOXIC CLEANING PRODUCTS TOO.

Write down how you feel when you spend time in your sacred space:

_____

_____

_____

_____

Lisa's musing

So, I'm not really a cleaner… but I love a clean house. This is one of the many things I chose to outsource many, many years ago. Tina the tidier (as we affectionately call her) has been with me for around 12 years. She is a dream. She loves it, and having her allows me to do things that I'm better at and love doing. I appreciate her each and every time she works her magic.

Looking for non-toxic cleaning products? Try Koala (**koala.eco**). They smell so amazing!

PHOTO SHOOT TIME! TAKE SOME PHOTOS OF YOUR SPACE AND THE THINGS IN IT, AND SAVE THEM TO YOUR PHONE FOR WHEN YOU NEED A VISUAL REMINDER TO GET YOU THROUGH A STRESSFUL DAY.

Share your pic with us #collectivehub and post it to our Facebook group: Collective Hub Club. We'd love to see your space.

Paste your pic here!

Lisa's musing

Little rewards. It's nice to capture your creativity and remind yourself how far you have come. Relish it and celebrate the fact you are taking time to really nourish yourself.

Have some fun with an online photo editor, **pixlr.com**.

IT'S EASY FOR YOUR SCARED SPACE (AND SELF-CARE IN GENERAL) TO GET PUSHED TO THE BOTTOM OF YOUR TO-DO LIST, SO TAKE TIME TODAY TO COMMIT TO HOW LONG YOU WILL SPEND IN YOUR SPACE AND WHEN. SCHEDULE IT IN YOUR DIARY AND WRITE IT DOWN ON THIS PAGE.

Make a commitment today. When will I use my sacred space?
For how long? What do I need to spend some time thinking over?

_____

_____

_____

_____

_____

_____

_____

Lisa's musing

Look at you go! Another month down! I hope you found
the past 30 days a soothing, nourishing and joyful experience.
Okay, next up, it's time to unplug ourselves.

*"Nourishing yourself in a way that helps you blossom in the direction
you want to go is attainable, and you are worth the effort."* – Deborah Day

june

UNPLUG YOURSELF

Digital devices have become ubiquitous, essential and integrated into our modern multi-screen, digital world. And, while we love our phone and laptop (a lot), it could be argued that they are the curse of modern life.

Our reliance on our digital digits is having an increasing affect on our sleep, health and even our posture! Yes, 'text neck' is an actual thing. This month, we want you to re-evaluate your relationship with your technology. Is it healthy? Is it what you want and need it to be?

Let's find out! It's the perfect opportunity to spend some time unplugged (eek!) so we can focus on our health, being mindful and connecting with our friends and family… without our phones being within arm's reach. We know this is going to be hard, and there are some challenges that will be difficult, but we ask you to bear with us as the rewards really do outweigh the effort.

JUNE 1

BEFORE YOU ATTEMPT THIS MONTH OF CHALLENGES, MAKE A LIST OF ACTIVITIES YOU CAN DO/WANT TO TRY THAT DON'T REQUIRE THE INTERNET OR YOUR PHONE. KEEP THAT LIST HANDY FOR WHEN YOU'RE 'BORED'.

What are 10 things you would like to try that do not involve technology?

_____

_____

_____

_____

_____

Okay, here we go. Some non-techy things I love to do are: picnic in the park, rock climbing, volunteering at Foodbank.org, paddleboarding, going to the golf driving range, a game of bocce or croquet (yep, we nerded out and bought both), beach volleyball, a doggy walk, jumping in the ocean, tennis, throwing a frisbee and sketching a landscape. What are yours?

"Put down your cell phones, put everything away, and feel your blood pulsing in you, feel your creative impulse, feel your own spirit, your heart, your mind. Feel the joy of being alive and free." – Patti Smith

---

JUNE 2

**PICK A MEDIA-FREE ROOM. EVEN IF IT'S JUST THE BATHROOM,
HAVE A TECH-FREE SANCTUARY SOMEWHERE IN THE HOME.**

Social media survey! Circle yes or no.

Do you feel anxious if you leave your phone in another room?
Yes   No

Do you read your newsfeed while watching TV?
Yes   No

Can you go a whole day without checking your social media?
Yes   No

Can you have a coffee with a friend and leave your phone in your bag?
Yes   No

We'll check back in at the end of this challenge and see how you are going.

Lisa's Musing

It definitely isn't the bathroom in our house! What is it with
boys and toilets and phones?! Hours of scrolling and, in his
case, watching pranks… our media-free zone is the bedroom.
My phone never makes it into the bedroom. There
has to be some down time.

*"People who smile while they are alone used to be called insane, until
we invented smartphones and social media."* – Mokokoma Mokhonoana

JUNE 3

TIME FOR A TECH DIARY. NOTE DOWN EVERY TIME YOU REACH FOR YOUR PHONE (YES, IT'S TEDIOUS, BUT WE HAVE A PURPOSE!) AND NOTE DOWN WHAT IT WAS FOR – WORK, EMAIL, INSTAGRAM, FACEBOOK, ETC. HAVE A LOOK AT THE LIST TONIGHT AND SEE WHERE YOUR PROBLEM AREAS ARE.

Track your phone pick-ups below:

_____

_____

_____

_____

_____

_____

Lisa's musing

Whoops! My hand is up. Guilty as charged. I have many problem areas. Time to step away from the 'gram; I'm way too reactive. I need to take back control and be more mindful and proactive in my phone dealings. Sometimes I just want to throw my phone in the sea.

Space App is designed to help users understand their phone usage, break phone addiction and find their phone-life balance.

JUNE 4

WHEN YOU'RE EXPOSED TO BRIGHT LIGHT IN THE EVENING, IT CAN DISRUPT PRODUCTION OF THE SLEEP HORMONE MELATONIN. TONIGHT, TURN OFF ALL YOUR DEVICES, TURN DOWN THE LIGHTS AND SPEND 30 MINUTES ON YOGA, READING OR TAKING A BATH BEFORE BED. SEE HOW IT AFFECTS YOUR SLEEP.

Sleep status: how long do you normally sleep?

What time do you normally go to bed and wake up?

What is a before-bed routine you can do to help you sleep?

Lisa's Musing

How often do we go straight from Netflix to checking Instagram just before we go to bed? I now put my phone on silent at about 8pm, step away and continue on with mindful, calming activities.

For sleep advice, check out sleep expert
Olivia Arezzolo, **oliviaarezzolo.com.au**.

START YOUR MORNING WITH A 15-MINUTE STRETCH INSTEAD OF A 15-MINUTE SCROLL.

List eight things you could do in the morning instead of wasting time on social media when you first wake up:

1. _____

2. _____

3. _____

4. _____

5. _____

6. _____

7. _____

8. _____

Lisa's musing

This is the nice thing about keeping my phone in the kitchen at night. I am not tempted to roll over and scroll. Instead, I keep a yoga mat at the foot of my bed and start the day with a few sun salutations.

Check out **stretching-exercises-guide.com** for a range of stretches you can easily do right at home.

VISIT A NEWSAGENT TODAY (REMEMBER THOSE?) AND BUY A BEAUTIFUL, GLOSSY MAGAZINE ON ANY TOPIC THAT MAKES YOU FEEL HAPPY. THEN DEVOTE SOME TIME TO READING IT WITH A CUP OF TEA SOMEWHERE COSY.

While reading your magazine, use the space below to jot down any notes or inspiration that floats into your head. Let your mind wonder a little.

Lisa's musing

This is music to my ears! As a magazine publisher and avid magazine reader, this is one of my most delicious indulgences. Please buy mags. It saddens me how thin they are getting (both in pagination and the number on the shelves).

Support a mag by subscribing to one directly or through isubscribe. Or, jump on to **collectivehub.com** to check out all 52 issues of *Collective Hub* magazine!

EAT ALL YOUR MEALS TODAY AWAY FROM A SCREEN - NO PHONES, TVS, LAPTOPS, KINDLES OR SCREENS OF ANY KIND. ENJOY THE QUIET, READ THE PAPER OR CATCH UP WITH FRIENDS OR FAMILY.

Love a picnic? So do we. List eight places you could eat lunch outside that are either close to home or your office.

1. _____

2. _____

3. _____

4. _____

5. _____

6. _____

7. _____

8. _____

Lisa's Musing

We try to do this most days. It's nice to consciously eat and catch up on the day with each other. If you live alone, try to read, sit on the balcony or in the garden, or just sit and ponder as you munch.

"Technology is a useful servant but a dangerous master." – Christian Lous Lange

CREATE TWO 'UNREACHABLE' PERIODS IN YOUR DAY WHEN YOU WON'T RESPOND TO MESSAGES OR CALLS. BLOCK THEM OUT IN YOUR DIARY AND REMEMBER TO SWITCH YOUR PHONE TO 'DO NOT DISTURB'.

Plan what you can do in these two periods today. It could be a list of things you've been meaning to do, listening to a podcast or simply getting your nails done. Treat these times like they are very important meetings.

_____

_____

_____

_____

Lisa's musing

I purposefully block out chunks of non-negotiable 'me time' in my diary, weeks in advance. I just mark it as private, so nobody knows what I'm doing at that time. When lots of people have access to your diary, trust me if it says something like 'massage' or 'gym', they will try to take that from you quicker than you can imagine!

"Technology is nothing. What's important is that you have a faith in people, that they're basically good and smart, and if you give them tools, they'll do wonderful things with them." – Steve Jobs

DO SOMETHING YOU LOVE TODAY. ANYTHING AT ALL. MAKE SURE IT MAKES YOU SMILE AND LAUGH AND FIND PURE HAPPINESS!

What do you truly, truly love? Write your top five favourite things below so that you capture them in one place.

1. _____

2. _____

3. _____

4. _____

5. _____

Lisa's Musing

Sometimes we become so used to doing things for others, that when we're asked what we love ourselves, it can be quite confronting. So, really feel into what it is that makes you super-duper happy. For me, it looks like a workout in the morning, a long lazy breakfast, a swim in the ocean, or sitting under an umbrella reading and dozing at the beach with close friends. Then a 90-minute deep-tissue massage. I'd finish up with cooking dinner at home and dancing into the night. Bliss.

Want to be adventurous? Try acrobatics! Find a class near you: **acrobaticdanceassociation.com.au.**

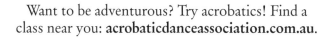

DELETE YOUR SOCIAL MEDIA APPS FROM YOUR PHONE (OR PUT THEM IN A HARD-TO-FIND OR LOCKED FOLDER). USE YOUR PHONE AS USUAL, BUT DON'T USE ANY SOCIAL MEDIA. IF YOU NEED TO CHECK, USE YOUR COMPUTER.

How does this affect your time on these apps?
How did that make you feel?

_____

_____

_____

_____

_____

Lisa's Musing

I can see you having a mini meltdown from here. It's okay. Trust me. This is hard to do. We are so attached to our phones, but once you do it, it's pure bliss. I have several friends who have done this for an entire month, and I did it myself for three weeks the last time I went to India. Oh, the liberation and freedom! You can do this.

Apps to help you control your phone addiction:
AppDetox, Flipd, OFFTIME.

TURN OFF YOUR SCREENS AND PHONE AS SOON AS IT'S DARK AND HAVE A LONG BATH/SHOWER, FOLLOWED BY READING A BOOK.

List eight things you can do tonight to help you sleep well:

1. _____

2. _____

3. _____

4. _____

5. _____

6. _____

7. _____

8. _____

Lisa's Musing

Pop some bath salts in, or if you're in the shower, spray some essential oils onto the walls. There is practically nothing better than the warmth on your body, followed by curling up with a good book. You'll sleep like a baby. Not a worry in the world. Sweet dreams, my friend.

Try **gleebooks.com.au** for a great selections of books to delve into.

VISIT A PLACE WHERE USING YOUR PHONE/TECHNOLOGY IS FROWNED UPON TODAY – THINK A YOGA STUDIO, THE LIBRARY, AN ART GALLERY OR EVEN A PLACE OF WORSHIP. PUT YOUR PHONE ON SILENT AND SEE HOW LONG YOU CAN REFRAIN FROM CHECKING IT.

List (or draw, for some down time) five places you could visit and look back on this page whenever you need a tech-free moment.

Lisa's Musing

Think of this as a forced vacation from your phone. How do you feel? Or, better still, reframe it: how free do you feel?!

For inspo, check out **earthtrekkers.com**.

**WRITE A LETTER OR A POSTCARD TO A FRIEND TODAY AND
POST IT TO THEM IN THE MAIL. OLD SCHOOL STYLE.**

Who would you like to write a letter to this year? Place their names
and addresses below. Mark them off as you send their letters.

Name: _____ Address: _____

Name: _____ Address: _____

Name: _____ Address: _____

Name: _____ Address: _____

Name: _____ Address: _____

Name: _____ Address: _____

Lisa's Musing

Never underestimate the power of snail mail. Most of what comes in
the post these days is junk, so think how much of a smile you will put
on a friend's face when they receive your handwritten letter! I make it
my mission to send at least a couple every week. I find out what people
are up to, what they've achieved, or even just send them a note out of
the blue to let them know how much I appreciate them.

*"Don't you like to write letters? I do because it's such a swell way to keep
from working and yet feel you've done something."* – Ernest Hemingway

GO FOR A WALK, RUN OR A COFFEE AND LEAVE YOUR PHONE AND SMART WATCH AT HOME. IT MIGHT SEEM HARD BUT THE 20 MINUTES OR SO OF SOLITUDE WILL HELP YOU FEEL LESS STRESSED.

Use the time like you would a meditation. If your mind starts wandering, remember that's okay, just bring it back to the present moment.

Post-run checklist: (circle yes or no)

Were you able to stay present?
Yes   No

Did you enjoy the break from your day?
Yes   No

Did you feel less stressed or calmer at the end of it?
Yes   No

Lisa's musing

So if it's running, this isn't going to happen for me. I absolutely need my beats or my little legs aren't going anywhere. Don't be hard on yourself, choose something that works for you. Just remember, if you're like me and pay for everything using Apple Pay on your phone, don't forget to take some cold hard cash or a credit card, so you don't get caught out!

Under Armour make some comfy shoes for walking and running. But my personal go to's since I started running more seriously are ASICS.

JUNE 15

BOOK IN FOR A MASSAGE OR MANI/PEDI TODAY AND UNPLUG
YOUR MIND FROM THE WORLD FOR A LITTLE WHILE.

Write a list of all the self-care 'treats' you'd like to do over
the next few weeks. Tick them off as you do them.

_____

_____

_____

_____

_____

_____

Lisa's Musing

Nothing better, and it doesn't need to be expensive. There are
massage places on almost every corner these days, and they seem
to cost somewhere around $60 to $90 for an hour. Likewise
mani/pedis are so much more accessible.

*"Self-care is one of the active ways that I love myself.
When you can and as you can, in ways that feel loving,
make time and space for yourself."* – Tracee Ellis Ross

LET'S TALK FACEBOOK. MOST OF US ARE ON IT FOR BUSINESS AND PERSONAL REASONS, BUT ONE AREA THAT CAN BE BOTH VERY HELPFUL AND ALSO OVERWHELMING IS GROUPS. TAKE A MOMENT TO GO THROUGH YOUR GROUPS AND DELETE ANY THAT DON'T SERVE YOU POSITIVELY.

Facebook assessment:
On a scale of one to 10, how enjoyable do you find Facebook?

How useful is it for you?

How essential is it for your day-to-day life?

How satisfied are you with Facebook?

How sad would you be if Facebook shut down tomorrow?

Lisa's Musing

The Social Dilemma on Netflix is great if you haven't seen it. While we have set up a Facebook group for recipients of this book, we're all about being very conscious about how we run it and what we create. We promise Collective Hub Club will be well worth keeping!

A quote that stuck with me from *The Social Dilemma*:
"If you're not paying for a product, you are the product."

DO SOMETHING REALLY FUN TODAY – BUY A BOOK, VISIT AN AQUARIUM, SEE A FRIEND. AND HERE'S THE KICKER: DON'T PUT IT ON SOCIAL MEDIA. AT ALL.

List some things you could do today and for the rest of this month, number them in order of preference. See if you can do them all before July.

_____

_____

_____

_____

_____

_____

Lisa's Musing

Just do it for you, not because you want to show it off to the world or prove that your life is fabulous. Just be purely indulgent and have this moment for you. I have a rule (you may have noticed) that I never share my partner or family on social media. It's just something I've consciously chosen to keep to myself. We all need to have something a little sacred. What will your something be?

Find something crazy to do on **adrenaline.com.au**.

CREATE A BED YOU'LL WANT TO DIVE INTO. CLEAR YOUR BEDSIDE TABLE, CHANGE YOUR SHEETS, SPRAY LAVENDER AND WEAR CLEAN PJS. TIME TO SWITCH OFF, READ, MEDITATE OR FOCUS ON YOUR DEEP BREATHING.

Write down everything you need in your bedside drawer, from your night cream to your reading glasses (if you have them!). Then clear out that drawer and move anything that isn't on your list to another place. That way you will feel calm and have everything you need at your fingertips.

_____

_____

_____

_____

_____

Lisa's Musing

I am a massive fan of linen sheets, soft throws, piles of cushions, essential oils and a good book on my bedside table. And (you may relate to this) my partner just does not get the cushion thing. He's practical. Doesn't dissuade me though.

Check out **@eadie_lifestyle, @bed.threads, @ilovelinen.**

REDESIGN YOUR DESKTOP ON YOUR COMPUTER SO THAT IT'S CLEAN AND EVERYTHING IS EITHER IN FOLDERS, OR FILED AWAY IN YOUR DOCUMENTS.

Take a moment to plan your desktop (yes, really)
so your computer will work for you and your lifestyle:

_____

_____

_____

_____

_____

_____

Lisa's Musing

You do not want to know how many folders I have my emails stored in. Okay, I'll humour you: I guestimate well over 400! I have everything filed meticulously by project and by client. It helps me feel organised and have everything at my fingertips. Everything else is stored on Google Docs, Dropbox and Asana.

Need help? Search 'Computer screen desktop organiser' on Etsy for downloadable images that can be useful for visual organising.

KEEP YOUR PHONE OUT OF SIGHT TODAY. NOT ON THE TABLE, COUCH OR YOUR DESK AND DEFINITELY NOT IN YOUR HAND. KEEP IT HIDDEN UNTIL YOU NEED TO USE IT, THEN PUT IT AWAY AGAIN AFTERWARDS.

Morning Q&A:
Do you think this will be an easy challenge?

Why? Will it affect the time you spend on your phone?

Evening Q&A:
How did this impact on your phone use?

Did you enjoy not having your phone in view? Why?

Lisa's Musing

I've been through stages (though I'm not currently in one) where I have actually had lockable phone boxes to put my phone in. I'd like to think I'm a bit more disciplined than needing one now. But do watch *The Social Dilemma* on Netflix if you haven't. There are very specific measures that companies take to keep us hooked, addicted and feeling a constant urge to pick up our phones.

Search 'kitchen safe: time locking container' on Amazon.

GO SCREEN-FREE FROM 8PM AND GET AN EARLY NIGHT'S SLEEP. USING TECHNOLOGY AFTER DARK CAN AFFECT OUR SLEEP PATTERNS, INTERFERE WITH OUR CIRCADIAN RHYTHMS AND INCREASE OUR STRESS LEVEL.

Scribble down 10 glorious phone-free activities you could do after 8pm. Hint: writing the activities here is one!

lisa's musing

Here are some of the most fun, non-tech things that I love to do at night. Cook up a big feast (it's a running joke… my partner always says 'how many are we expecting?' What can I say, I specialise in big numbers), play a board game (my faves at the moment are Catan and Risk), play Jenga, curl up with a good book, journal, meditate, do some yin yoga, go for a moonlit walk, soak in the bath, do a crossword, or come up with ideas for a new project. The options are endless!

Check out the games section of **theiconic.com.au** for an amazing collection you can buy.

ON YOUR COMMUTE, DURING YOUR MORNING COFFEE OR BASICALLY ANY TIME YOU MIGHT REACH FOR YOUR PHONE THIS MORNING, LISTEN TO A PODCAST INSTEAD OR BURY YOUR NOSE IN A GOOD BOOK.

Write down the five podcasts or books you'd like to
listen to or read, then check them off once you have.

1. _____

2. _____

3. _____

4. _____

5. _____

Lisa's Musing

Can I cheekily recommend a good one? Mine! Hear me RAW.
I have wonderful, inspiring guests every week talking mostly through
a business lens about obstacles they have had to overcome, and what
has made them who they are. I love recording them and I hope you love
listening to them. Share your thoughts with me #collectivehub or send
a post on our Facebook group: Collective Hub Club!

~~~~

Check out these great podcasts, *Ladies, We Need To Talk*, by Yumi
Styles, *Crappy to Happy* by clinical psychologist Cass Dunn and
Healthy Her by Amelia Phillips.

LOOK AFTER YOUR MENTAL HEALTH BY BLOCKING WORDS OR PHRASES ON INSTAGRAM AND TWITTER. YOU COULD EVEN TURN OFF COMMENTS IF YOU FEEL THEY ARE A SOURCE OF STRESS.

Write a list of words, phrases or hashtags that make you feel sad, anxious or angry on social media.

If you need more space, transfer this list to a journal or a spare sheet of paper.

Lisa's Musing

Let's face it, social media is relentless. It's constant. While it's an imperative for business and connection, I'm trying to step away and, as hard as it is, relinquish some control and responsibility to my team. I've always felt I have to respond to everything and everyone, but now my team often do. They'll always sign off as them, not me, to remain authentic, but it does feel a little liberating and gives me time and space to focus on growth and my personal priorities.

If you feel like chatting to a psychologist, but don't want to do it in person, find one for an online chat at **welysn.com**.

JUNE 24

COMMIT TO READING FOR AT LEAST 30 MINUTES BEFORE BEDTIME TONIGHT, THEN INDULGE IN A 10-MINUTE GUIDED MEDITATION. NO SCREENS AFTER 9PM.

What did you read?

What do you like about this book?

How did it make you feel?

Lisa's Musing

Reading takes us to a different place and time. Even if you just dip into a few pages. Find inspiration everywhere.

~~~

"The library is inhabited by spirits that come out of the pages at night." – Isabel Allende

WRITE A LIST OF ALL THE REASONS YOU LOVE YOUR PHONE AND COMPUTER. LIST EVERYTHING FROM STORING YOUR PHOTOS TO SOCIAL MEDIA. NOW WRITE DOWN ALL THE REASONS YOU DON'T LIKE THEM. HOW CAN YOU MANAGE THESE ASPECTS OF THE LOVE/HATE RELATIONSHIP?

Likes:

_____

_____

_____

_____

_____

Dislikes:

_____

_____

_____

_____

_____

Lisa's Musing

Anyone else feeling the pull? This is a great exercise, because if you're like me, it really is a love/hate relationship. It's good to have an awareness around what we love, what's useful, what we can't live without and, conversely, what we really don't like, what is a time waster, and what we really can live without.

Curl up and watch 'LIKE' a documentary about
social media that is unforgettable (**thelikemovie.com**).

THROW (OR PLAN) A DINNER PARTY, AND ASK EVERYONE TO CHECK THEIR PHONES AT THE DOOR, OR HAVE LUNCH WITH FRIENDS AND ASK EVERYONE TO PUT THEIR PHONES OUT OF SIGHT. THE FIRST PERSON TO REACH FOR THEIRS HAS TO DO A SOLO DANCE SESSION IN FRONT OF EVERYBODY.

Write down which friends you'll invite and any tech rules or punishments!

_____

_____

_____

_____

_____

_____

Lisa's Musing

If you're having dinner at mine, let me give you a red-hot tip: there is time for a quick Insta story of my food (yes, it's that good!), but then phones need to be put away. I'm all about togetherness, being present and having deep conversations and crazy amounts of belly laughs. No phones needed.

Deakin University has a great quiz called 'Are you addicted to your smartphone?' Search 'smartphone' at **this.deakin.edu.au**.

TIME FOR SOME NATURE TODAY: LET'S GROUND OURSELVES ONCE MORE. WALK BAREFOOT (TECH-FREE) ON SAND, DIRT, GRASS – ANYTHING NATURAL – AND LET YOUR FEET SOAK UP THE GOODNESS OF MOTHER NATURE.

What are your childhood memories of being in nature? Did you spend time in parks, beaches, or hiking? What do you remember about these moments? Write about your memories below:

_____

_____

_____

_____

_____

Liza's Musing

Whenever I am in nature, I try to take off my shoes to feel the sand beneath my toes. The salt on my ankles. The grittiness of rocks under my feet (like a free massage!). The coolness of grass. For me, it automatically makes me feel grounded, alive, safe and calm, and I just seem to let out a big sigh of relief. Breathe. Back to basics.

"I love walking in the woods, on the trails, along the beaches. I love being part of nature. I love walking alone. It is therapy. One needs to be alone, to recharge one's batteries." – Grace Kelly

TAKE YOURSELF ON A 'TECH-FREE DATE' AND LEAVE YOUR PHONE IN YOUR BAG OR EVEN AT HOME. CHOOSE YOUR FAVOURITE CAFE, BEACH, RESERVE OR PLACE AND ENJOY SOME 'ME' TIME, SCREEN-FREE.

Write yourself an invitation to the date. Yes, we are serious.
Explain where you will take yourself and then give three reasons
why you deserve a little pampering and TLC.

_____

_____

_____

_____

_____

Lisa's musing

You will be surprised what you see. Yesterday I went for a walk and took a photo of Tamarama Beach. Do you know what? Three people contacted me with similar messages: 'Wow, wings in the sky'. I was so busy getting the perfect shot that I didn't stop to enjoy the reality. Only after seeing their comments did I realise that the clouds really did look like angel wings. Note to self (and all of us): stop, breathe and take it all in. Don't just snap for the grid!

Find out more about dating yourself at **eharmony.com.au** (yes, really). Their article, '5 Reasons to 'Date' Yourself', is an excellent resource!

JUNE 29

CALL A FRIEND FOR A CHAT TODAY. TRY TO MAKE IT A PHONE CALL, NOT A ZOOM OR VIDEO CHAT. WE CAN FOCUS MUCH MORE ON WORDS WHEN WE HAVEN'T GOT A SCREEN TO DISTRACT US.

Think of three friends you should call over the few next weeks.

Name:

I should call because:

Name:

I should call because:

Name:

I should call because:

Lisa's musing

I just called my sister. It was such a great way to switch off to the world and be in the moment. Our call went for an hour and 40 minutes. We had nothing to distract us and the conversation just weaved from one subject to the next. I felt so uplifted and happy when we hung up.

"Friendship is born at that moment when one person says to another, 'What! You too? I thought I was the only one." – C.S. Lewis

JUNE 30

ONE FINAL TASK THIS MONTH! TURN OFF ALL YOUR NOTIFICATIONS ON YOUR PHONE TODAY (AND MAYBE PERMANENTLY?) AND SEE WHAT LIFE IS LIKE WITHOUT THE CONSTANT PINGING OF MESSAGES AND LIKES. IT'S A LOT CALMER, LET ME TELL YOU!

Social media survey update!

Now we have reached the end of the month, let's see how you answer the same questions as at the beginning of this challenge. Notice how your answers have changed. Circle yes or no below and then write a sentence about how you've improved (or what you can do to be better!).

Do you feel anxious if you leave your phone in another room?   Yes   No

Do you read your newsfeed while watching TV?   Yes   No

Can you go a whole day without checking your social media?   Yes   No

Can you have a coffee with a friend and not touch your phone?   Yes   No

Lisa's Musing

Well, here's a tip. I have no notifications on my phone at all except text messages. I don't even have them on my WhatsApp. I recently added Shopify (that's addictive enough when you've finally figured out how to run a pretty serious e-commerce business after 19 years!). But that's it. No interruptions. Zero. Zilch. Unless I choose them.

"Focus on how to be social, not on how to do social." – Jay Baer

Use the space below to reflect on your month of being unplugged. Write anything that comes to mind, both positive and negative, and think about what you'll take into next month and for the rest of the year (and maybe even forever!).

_____

_____

_____

_____

_____

july

FIND CONFIDENCE

Self-belief is one of those intangible possessions that can really make the difference between being where you are and being where you want to be. And at the heart of it, is a little thing called confidence.

Even the most successful entrepreneurs, top athletes and most 'out there' celebrities, all work on their self-belief and confidence.

So, whether you are outgoing and boisterous or quiet and shy (or a combination of the two), boosting your own self-belief can improve your resilience, reduce stress and overcome any obstacles.

Plus, you'll be able to achieve more of what you want.

The next four weeks will focus on building up your self-esteem, improving your confidence, and helping you learn to love yourself as much as we love you!

ASK YOURSELF THIS QUESTION: WHAT DO PEOPLE COME TO YOU FOR WHEN THEY NEED HELP OR ADVICE? THESE ARE THE QUALITIES YOU WERE GIFTED WITH.

Make a list of some of the ways you have helped others – this could be friends, workmates, family or even strangers.

Lisa's musing

For me, it's about confidence or connection. They want to know how I became so confident (years of therapy and really working on getting to know myself), and can I connect them with someone to do XYZ? People also come to me for ideas and problem solving. I think laterally and come up with solutions quickly.

"Confidence is everything. Confidence is what makes that simple white tee and jeans look good." – Ciara

TIME TO REGROUP: WHAT GIVES YOU CONFIDENCE? SPEND A MOMENT TODAY THINKING ABOUT YOURSELF AND WHERE YOUR CONFIDENCE COMES FROM.

What are some moments in your life when you felt most confident? Who was there, why did you feel confident, what were the elements that helped to make you feel confident? List them below and if you're feeling extra confident, share them with us #collectivehub or post in our Facebook group Collective Hub Club.

_____

_____

_____

_____

_____

_____

Lisa's musing

The trick is to stop seeing 'confidence' as a feeling that comes from external validation. We need to keep honing the tools so we truly understand ourselves, and can start to get internally confident despite, not because of, what others think of us.

Check out Mr Confidence himself for ideas on this: **tonyrobbins.com/building-confidence**.

JULY 3

SELF-REFLECTION AUDIT: TIME TO THINK ABOUT THE TIMES IN YOUR LIFE WHERE YOU FELT A LACK OF CONFIDENCE.

What happened to make you feel insecure, how did you react, and how could you have changed that or reacted differently?

_____

_____

_____

_____

_____

_____

_____

_____

Lisa's Musing

I wasn't always confident. I had low self esteem. I know for sure that when we dig deep and understand our triggers, we can learn to be confident and self assured.

"Confidence is contagious. So is lack of confidence." – Vince Lombardi

WHO ARE YOU? TAKE A MOMENT TODAY TO
WRITE DOWN WHO YOU REALLY ARE.

What are your strengths, what are your weaknesses. Think about what makes you uniquely you. Think about what you value and what's important to you.

_____

_____

_____

_____

_____

Lisa's musing

This is a big one, and I understand that sometimes going inward can be a little uncomfortable, and even confronting. To truly ask, who am I? What's important to me? What makes me happy? What makes me tick? I started my journey for truth as a dedicated seeker in 2004, and I've been on the path ever since. Sometimes it's hard, but the more we get to truly know ourselves, the more confident we become.

Try the personality test at **gimmemore.com** to give you some insight into your strengths.

STAND TALL: SPEND TODAY ON YOUR POSTURE. STAND TALL ALL DAY AND SEE HOW IT CHANGES YOUR CONFIDENCE AS A RESULT.

A great yoga pose for this is Mountain Pose; it uses nearly every muscle and is a very powerful posture.

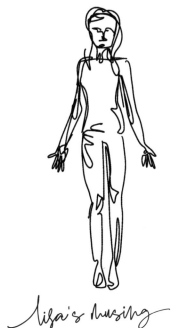

Lisa's Musing

Such a simple exercise, but do it. How much better does it make you feel? It's a bit of a 'fake it till you make it' exercise. Let's do this.

Search "mountain pose" on YouTube for a demonstration on how to do it properly.

SLOW IT DOWN: SPEND TODAY CONCENTRATING ON SPEAKING MORE SLOWLY AND NOT RUSHING AROUND. AS A RESULT, YOU'LL FIND YOUR SENTENCES MORE CONSIDERED, AUTHORITATIVE AND CONFIDENT, AND YOU'LL FIND YOU TEND TO BE LESS STRESSED.

A great exercise for this is to record yourself saying three things you will do today. Then do another recording trying to say them a little slower, and a final one taking pauses, and relaxing as you speak. Look at each recording and see which one sounds best on replay. Do one final recording tonight before bed, when you are relaxed and tired. Compare them below!

Recording 1:

Recording 2:

Recording 3:

Recording 4:

Lisa's Musing

I am stepping away from this page sheepishly… Just kidding. I'm going to own it: I speak fast. My brain works fast. Words come out a million miles an hour – but there are definitely situations where I have had to consciously slow down (podcasts, TV, public speaking). The powers of the pause… and also what comes out of my mouth… are so much clearer and cleverer as a result.

The Speech Pacesetter app can help with learning how to speak slower.

FLAUNT YOURSELF: WHAT'S YOUR FAVOURITE PHYSICAL ASSET? YOUR FEET, YOUR LEGS, YOUR EARS?! DRESS TO SHOW IT OFF.

Write down all the parts of your body that you like and why:

1. _____

2. _____

3. _____

4. _____

5. _____

Lisa's Musing

I'm going with feet, legs and hair here! What did you have? By the way, I just started following **@trainwithjoan** on Instagram. Oh my gosh… inspired! She was a self-confessed couch potato and at 70 she started weight lifting. Her turnaround is impressive and inspirational. If we're not feeling great, any one of us (at any time) can take control and do something about it!

"It's impossible to be stylish without confidence, you see." – Jane Birkin

BE PREPARED: DO YOU HAVE A MEETING, SOCIAL ENGAGEMENT OR CLASS TODAY? THE EASIEST WAY TO BE CONFIDENT IS TO KNOW YOUR STUFF; SPEND FIVE MINUTES RESEARCHING THE TOPIC/RESTAURANT/PERSON YOU'RE MEETING SO YOU CAN ASK MEANINGFUL, CONFIDENT QUESTIONS.

What research do you need to do? What questions can you ask?

I say five minutes because that works for me. It's a skill I have honed and honed over the years. I can take in a lot of information very quickly to prep for something, but if you need longer, don't beat yourself up. Other very successful people I know (my partner for one) will spend at least an hour prepping for most things. And if it's important and unfamiliar territory to me I'll also spend more time. Learning is magic. And knowledge is power.

Learn how to speed read and do your research faster at **spreeder.com**.

PRACTICE EYE CONTACT: ONE THING ALL CONFIDENT PEOPLE HAVE IN COMMON IS THE ABILITY TO HOLD EYE CONTACT. IT'S SURPRISINGLY HARD.

Ask a friend to help you with this: sit and look into each other's eyes. Then describe some positive things about each other. Write them down here.

1. _____

2. _____

3. _____

4. _____

5. _____

Lisa's Musing

One of the many wacky things I have done in the name of self development is to stare for 20 minutes into the eyes of a stranger. Just to sit still and quiet and stare. To see and be seen.

For eye contact tips, see **medium.com** for a great article.

LOOK AT YOURSELF IN THE MIRROR FOR ONE MINUTE: CONFIDENT PEOPLE DON'T USE NEGATIVE SELF TALK OR LAMENT THE BAGS UNDER THEIR EYES WHEN THEY LOOK IN THE MIRROR – THEY JUST SEE THE BODY THEY'RE THANKFUL FOR HAVING.

Start by looking yourself straight in the eyes in the mirror.
Then write down six positive words to describe your experience.

1. _____

2. _____

3. _____

4. _____

5. _____

6. _____

Lisa's Musing

I am very careful about my 'languaging'. My positive self talk. I am a big believer that what we speak becomes reality. So, if something negative is about to pop out, stop and consciously flip it into a positive.

"Loving or hating the life you are living is solely all in your repeated self-talk." – Edmond Mbiaka

JULY 11

SOMETIMES A GOOD, LONG LAUGH IS ENOUGH TO HELP YOU TO FEEL CONFIDENT. THREE TIMES THROUGHOUT THE DAY TODAY, WATCH A SHORT CLIP FROM ONE OF YOUR FAVOURITE SHOWS OR FUNNY PEOPLE.

Write down six shows or comedians that will make you laugh every time – then refer back to this page when you need a lift.

1. _____

2. _____

3. _____

4. _____

5. _____

6. _____

Lisa's musing

Laughter is the best. My purest essence is joy, and there is nothing better than when those uncontrollable belly laughs happen. I laugh at most things most days. I hope that, when I'm 90, I have lines all over my face that show just how much I've loved and laughed.

"Nothing is worth more than laughter. It is strength to laugh and to abandon oneself, to be light." – Frida Kahlo

SPEND FIVE MINUTES IN THE WONDER WOMAN STANCE: STUDIES SHOW IT CAN ACTUALLY MAKE YOU FEEL MORE CONFIDENT. DO IT BEFORE MEETINGS, OR SITUATIONS WHERE YOU NEED TO BE ON YOUR A-GAME.

This pose is struck by standing tall with legs wider than hip-width apart and hands or fists placed on the hips. Don't forget to straighten your back! Write down five words that capture how you feel after doing this pose.

_____

_____

_____

_____

_____

Lisa's Musing

This will make you feel stronger, taller, more confident – and you can have a little giggle at yourself at the end. Win, win, win, I say. By the way, if you want to go one step further, hang out with kids and really step up the role! I just bought a ladybug costume to match my four-year-old niece. So now we both feel invincible.

Find instructions for yoga poses at **yogajournal.com**

**DECIDE ON A SET OF EMPOWERING RULES FOR YOURSELF.
PERHAPS ONE IS ABOUT YOUR RELATIONSHIPS, BOUNDARIES,
WORK, THE WAY YOU TREAT PEOPLE AND THE PEOPLE YOU DECIDE
ARE YOUR FRIENDS. THESE ARE YOUR RULES TO LIVE BY.**

Write them down on this page, sign it and commit to them.

_____

_____

_____

_____

_____

Sign here: _____

Lisa's Musing

I have strong non-negotiables about my boundaries. What is okay
and what is not okay. When I have 'me' time. The things I look for in
friendships. Things that empower me and disempower me. I am the
queen of lists and journalling (hence this book). I find writing it down
helps me get so much clearer on how I truly want to live my life.

*"Confidence comes from hours and days and weeks and years
of constant work and dedication"* – Robert Staubach

COLLABORATE WITH A FRIEND ON A NEW PROJECT – IT COULD BE A HOBBY OR A WORK-RELATED IDEA. WORKING WITH SOMEONE WILL HELP YOU RECOGNISE HOW MUCH YOU BRING TO THE COLLABORATION.

Write a list of friends you'd love to collaborate with, and some ideas on how.

Friend: How I would like to collaborate with them:

_____   _____

_____   _____

_____   _____

_____   _____

_____   _____

Lisa's Musing

It is so much fun coming up with ideas, dreaming big and exploring possibilities. It can take you down many exciting rabbit holes. I would stress that if you're going to do something even slightly serious, get some clear roles and responsibilities in place in writing. It saves all sorts of heartache and resentment down the track.

To find lots of people to collaborate with, see **collabosaurus.com**.

GO THROUGH YOUR WARDROBE AND PULL OUT ANY WORK OR GOING OUT CLOTHES YOU DON'T FEEL CONFIDENT, STRONG AND SEXY IN. WHAT WE WEAR REFLECTS WHO WE ARE, HOW WE FEEL AND HOW WE WANT TO BE TREATED. DO YOU NEED SOME NEW POWER CLOTHES?

Use the space below to list the items you want to buy.

_____   _____

_____   _____

_____   _____

_____   _____

_____   _____

Lisa's musing

When I had an office (I now do this with my partner or my team on Zoom), I would pick out an outfit I was unsure about and wear it for a day. I would notice how it made me feel (first and foremost), but then play a game of 'hit or miss' with my team. It's amazing how many pieces I've revived this way and, more importantly, how many I've rehomed. Be gone clothes that don't make us feel fab!

"The most beautiful thing you can wear is confidence." – Blake Lively

JULY 16

SELFIE-LOVE. TODAY WE'RE ASKING YOU TO TAKE A SELFIE AND POST IT ON SOCIAL MEDIA. USE A FILTER IF YOU WANT, BUT THE POINT IS TO BE COMFORTABLE SHARING WHO YOU ARE WITH THE WORLD.

Write down how you feel after posting your selfie to social media. Don't forget to tag us #collectivehub or post it to our Facebook group: Collective Hub Club – we'd love to see you!

One of my new fave Insta accounts is @thebirdspapaya. Sarah has an inspiring story and her feed is a journal of life and love after massive change. Check her out before you post. Then get brave.

For selfie tips, search 'selfie' in the articles tab on **influenster.com**.

REFLECT TODAY ON ANY COMPLIMENTS YOU HAVE RECEIVED LATELY – THESE COULD BE FROM COLLEAGUES, FRIENDS, COMMENTS ON SOCIAL MEDIA, FEEDBACK AFTER A BUSINESS MEETING. IF YOU CAN'T REMEMBER ANY, TEXT A FEW FRIENDS AND ASK THEM FOR SOME. YES, IT'S BALLSY. BUT THIS MONTH IS ALL ABOUT CONFIDENCE, DON'T FORGET!

Use these to build a list of qualities for yourself. Write down all these qualities in the space below. Circle the ones that mean a lot to you, underline ones you want to work on, and star any that you are especially proud of.

Lisa's Musings

Life certainly isn't about external validation, but it is great to start noticing the things that people say about you. Rather than sheepishly brushing them off, start to consciously take note. They may be things you didn't realise about yourself and strengths that you can play to.

Record yourself saying daily affirmations with
My Affirmations: Live Positive app.

POSITIVITY PLUS: WRITE DOWN FIVE THINGS THAT ARE CHALLENGES RIGHT NOW. THESE COULD BE SITUATIONS OR PEOPLE THAT ARE FRUSTRATING YOU, WORLD EVENTS, HOME LIFE. THEN REFRAME YOUR LIST AND REWRITE IT IN A POSITIVE VOICE. WHAT CAN YOU SEE THAT IS POSITIVE IN EACH SITUATION?

1. _____
2. _____
3. _____
4. _____
5. _____

1. _____
2. _____
3. _____
4. _____
5. _____

Lisa's Musing

This is about learning to mindset flip and see the silver linings.
A technique I taught myself years ago. Reframing to an 'attitude of gratitude'. It's not always easy, but always worth it. Notice your energy when you stay in the negative, and then the shift when you go to the positive. Just yesterday someone really did something wrong by me. It was disloyal and dishonest. I fumed for a while, and then I let it fuel me to become bigger, better, stronger. I left that energy where it belonged. Well and truly behind me.

A good book for this is *Curveballs: How to Keep It Together When Life Tries to Tear You a New One* by Emma Markezic.

NOTHING MAKES YOU FEEL MORE CONFIDENT THAN GIVING OUT COMPLIMENTS LIKE CANDY. CHOOSE FRIENDS, STRANGERS, WORK COLLEAGUES, ANYONE THAT DESERVES A LITTLE PICK-ME-UP.

Write down five words to describe how you felt after giving a compliment:

Lisa's musing

This is one of the easiest and most gratifying things to do and it's extraordinary how this selfless act actually really impacts the person we are complimenting. Do it for the right reason though, not so you can feel good – that's just a nice bi-product.

"Compliments cost nothing, yet many pay dear for them." – Thomas Fuller

IS THERE A SPECIFIC AREA WHERE YOU ARE LACKING CONFIDENCE? HOW CAN YOU EXPAND YOUR EXPERTISE IN THIS AREA?

Write down some of the skills you'd like to improve and how you could improve them. Is there a course you could do, or do you need to seek advice?

Skill: How I can improve:

_____   _____

_____   _____

_____   _____

_____   _____

_____   _____

Lisa's musing

The great thing is there are so many free online courses, YouTube videos and even universities that now enable you to study your own path at your own pace. So make a list of things that fascinate you and that you'd like to try. Then pick one and go for it.

For free video tutorials, check out **shortcourses.unsw.edu.au**.

THERE IS GREAT POWER IN BEING ABLE TO LAUGH AT YOURSELF. USE THIS PAGE TO DO A PERSONAL ROAST OF YOU – WHAT CAN YOU FIND FUNNY ABOUT YOUR FAULTS, OBSESSIONS, LIKES AND LOVES?

Scribble some phrases from your roast here. Did you make yourself laugh?

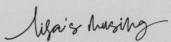

Oh, where do I start with this one! I am permanently laughing at the ridiculousness of so many things I do. When you laugh at yourself and don't take anything too seriously it makes life so much more fun! I'm obsessive about odd things, like not drinking out of the same glass as someone else. I love any kids' movies that are girly feel-good things that are really for 8 to 12-year-olds, I'm sure. I punch the air when I run, much to the hysteria of passers-by. I could go on and on.

Watch *How Laughing at Yourself Can Change the World*, a TED talk by Brad Jenkins.

TALK TO A NEW PERSON. IT COULD BE SOMEONE AT THE GYM OR YOUR BARISTA. PULLING YOURSELF OUT OF YOUR COMFORT ZONE STRETCHES YOUR CONFIDENCE QUICKER THAN YOU CAN SAY, "HI!"

Write down who you spoke to and how it made you feel.

_____

_____

_____

_____

_____

_____

_____

Lisa's Musing

I did this today in a homewares store. I asked the saleswoman about her day. I could tell how much she enjoyed talking. When I left the store she said "you have such great energy," but, in fact, it was her energy that was bringing everything. I simply took the time to connect.

For 50 ideas of how to get out of your comfort zone, search 'comfort zone' at **healthyhappyimpactful.com**.

TONIGHT BEFORE BED, WRITE DOWN THE THINGS THAT YOU DID WELL, FELT GOOD ABOUT OR WERE PROUD OF YOURSELF FOR DOING TODAY. GIVE YOURSELF A HIGH FIVE FOR NAILING THOSE THINGS AND FEEL THE POSITIVE VIBES AS YOU DRIFT OFF TO SLEEP.

List them here:

_____

_____

_____

_____

_____

lisa's musing

These can be anything. Here are some thought starters from me: I made three batches of banana bread to take to my big Italian family and delivered them to their doorsteps. I did a solid hour of training, and although it nearly killed me at the time, it felt sooooo good afterwards! I got through writing 40 of these little musings today. Yippee! It's a good day to have a good day. Three of my values – family, wellness, community. Tick, tick, tick.

"Confidence isn't optimism or pessimism, and it's not a character attribute. It's the expectation of a positive outcome." – Rosabeth Moss Kanter

**WRITE THIS MANTRA ON A PIECE OF PAPER AND PUT IT
ON YOUR MIRROR: 'I AM BRAVE. I AM STRONG. I AM SMART.
I AM BEAUTIFUL. I AM CONFIDENT. I'VE GOT THIS.'**

Use the space below to write down other personal mantras that you love.

_____

_____

_____

_____

_____

_____

Liza's musing

If you get stuck, check out my book of Daily Mantras – there
are 365 of them, compiled by moi. There are so many people going
through that book together on a daily basis now, and there's something
super-duper powerful in that. I hope this book is doing the same!

Oprah.com has a great article on creating your own personal mantra.

JULY 25

PRACTICE YOUR 'ELEVATOR PITCH'. WRITE DOWN YOUR RESPONSE TO THE QUESTION, "TELL ME A LITTLE BIT ABOUT YOURSELF". TALK ABOUT WHO YOU ARE, WHAT YOU DO, WHAT YOUR PASSIONS ARE. RECORD YOURSELF AND WATCH IT BACK (IT'LL BE HARD AT FIRST). ONCE YOU HAVE THIS DOWN, YOU'LL FEEL SUPER CONFIDENT ANY TIME YOU NEED TO ROLL IT OUT.

Write down your final version and share it with us at #collectivehub or post it in our Facebook group (Collective Hub Club) so we can all cheer you along!

_____

_____

_____

_____

_____

_____

Lisa's musing

Okay, here's mine (in a business sense) to help you out: "I'm an entrepreneur for entrepreneurs, living my life out loud, showing that anything is possible. I provide tools and resources to inspire and educate others to live their best life."

There's a cute YouTube tutorial by Lauren Berger on how to create your 30-second elevator pitch: **youtube.com/c/internqueen**.

CHANGE A SMALL HABIT. WRITE DOWN SIX HABITS YOU COULD START, LIKE GET UP 15 MINUTES EARLIER, DRINK EIGHT GLASSES OF WATER OR CALL YOUR MUM. ONCE YOU'VE GOT YOUR LIST, CHOOSE ONE TO START WITH TODAY.

List your six habits below:

1. _____

2. _____

3. _____

4. _____

5. _____

6. _____

Lisa's musing

This book is full of them. And we're now almost three-quarters of the way through – so if you get stuck, go back through the pages to give you thought starters and reminders. One of mine is quitting sugar. Another is exercising every day. And drinking more water (I am a sipper), I need to drink a lot more consciously.

"Action is a great restorer and builder of confidence. Inaction is not only the result, but the cause, of fear." – Norman Vincent Peale

SPEND SOME TIME TODAY RETHINKING AND REWRITING YOUR TO-DO LIST. BREAK THINGS DOWN INTO SMALL TASKS, PRIORITISE AND CULL. WE ARE ONLY AS CONFIDENT AS OUR TO-DO LISTS MAKES US FEEL.

Use this page to split your list into 'high, mid and low' priority'.

High priority	Mid priority	Low priority

Lisa's Musing

I write an overarching to-do list before the start of every month with my 10 major goals. Then, every night, I write my daily to-do list for the following day. Everything on it circles back to the big things I want to achieve. This makes it achievable in bite-sized, actionable pieces.

Check out todoist.com for a great tool to help with to-do lists.

CLEAR YOUR DESK, DESKTOP OR MOBILE. HAVING A CLEAR SPACE WILL HELP MAKE YOU FEEL MORE ORGANISED AND MORE CONFIDENT.

Write down here the reasons you like the work you do. If you can't think of at least five, perhaps you need to shift your focus.

_____

_____

_____

_____

_____

Lisa's musing

I inherited a not-so-great trait from my father (thanks, Dad). He was the ultimate hoarder and had clutter everywhere! So, it's not a natural tendency for me to have a clean and tidy workspace. But I do it and I feel so much better when I do. It just takes a bit more effort than your average Joe for me to get there. Now, why I love what I do: I'm living 100 per cent on purpose. I love living a big life. I love pushing myself. I love helping others and seeing their extraordinary results. I love the flexibility of my lifestyle. I love creating content and writing. I could go on and on and on…

Find lots of organisation advice at **mindtools.com.**

DO ONE THING YOU'VE BEEN PUTTING OFF TODAY. WE ALL HAVE THOSE LITTLE JOBS ON OUR TO-DO LIST THAT KEEP GETTING FORGOTTEN. MAYBE IT'S BOOKING THE DENTIST, MAYBE IT'S CLEANING YOUR CAR... WHATEVER IT IS, YOU WILL FEEL LIKE A QUEEN OR KING ONCE IT'S DONE.

Use the space below to scribble down all those things you've been putting off. Now circle one and do it today! Try to get through the rest of them over the next month.

Lisa's musing

Oh, dentists! Poo! No offence to any dentists reading this, I'm sure you are lovely, I just don't enjoy visiting the dentist. But, do make lists of all the things you just need to get done (boring. Yawn. Blah). Write them down. Do them first thing. Tick them off. Then the rest of the day can only get a whole lot better!

～～～～

"I have a confidence about my life that comes from standing tall on my own two feet." – Jane Fonda

WE FOCUS ON THIS A LOT, BUT EXERCISING MAKES YOU FEEL GOOD. SO SPEND SOME TIME TODAY DOING A CLASS, STRETCHING, GOING FOR A RUN, ANYTHING THAT WILL WORK YOUR BODY AND RELEASE THAT SEROTONIN!

Use the space below to explore how you feel before and after your workout.

_____

_____

_____

_____

_____

_____

Lisa's musing

If you're like me, sometimes it's a bit of a slog getting there, but once I am there (and afterwards), I feel so damn great. Every single time I say to myself, "I've got to do this more often." It makes me feel strong and alive, gives me a great sense of accomplishment, and just makes me feel fitter and more confident. Every single time!

Find a new exercise class near you at **mindbody.com.au**.

JULY 31

SMILE! IT WORKS EVERY TIME TO GIVE YOU CONFIDENCE. SMILE AS YOU WALK ALONG THE STREET, HOP ON A BUS, PAY FOR PARKING, ARRIVE AT WORK. YOU WON'T ALWAYS GET A SMILE BACK, BUT THIS MINDFUL FOCUS ON SMILING WILL HELP YOU FEEL AND LOOK MORE CONFIDENT.

Write or draw the things that make you smile below:

Lisa's Musing

I'm doing it right now. Sitting here by myself in my home office (aka third bedroom), and straight away it's making me feel perkier, happier, more alive. Just try it. Also… yesterday I saw one of our Italian rellies. She is 95, and you know what? Her whole face smiles! Her eyes smile. Her mouth is always turned up. I reckon she's been smiling her whole life. And it shows. I can't get enough of her. Thank you, Therese.

"A smile is the best make-up any girl can wear." – Marilyn Monroe

august

THE POWER OF NO

This is a biggie. Are you ready? We are about to get comfortable with saying one of the hardest sentences in the English language… No.

And yes, that is a complete sentence. We are all natural people pleasers – but saying "yes" to things we don't have time or energy for creates feelings of guilt, stress and sometimes even anger.

It can mean that we end up having to say no to ourselves later on, or no to other things we'd actually prefer to do. It can mean that we end up being around people who might not be good for us, or sometimes doing projects that don't align with our core values.

Saying "no" isn't selfish. It's not something you should feel guilty about. It simply means, "I don't have the time/capacity/energy/ willingness to do this for you." Try it. It's liberating!

AUGUST 1

FIRST AND FOREMOST, STOP SAYING YES WHEN YOU WANT TO SAY NO! TODAY, CONSCIOUSLY MOVE THROUGH THE DAY AND NOTICE HOW MANY PEOPLE ASK SOMETHING OF YOU WHERE YOU COULD SAY NO.

At the end of the day write down how many
times you said yes but wanted to say no.

_____

_____

_____

_____

_____

Lisa's musing

Funny thing is, I opened my computer to write and my sister rang.
That in and of itself isn't that funny, except that the first of August is
her birthday (shout out to @curlykatemessenger today). As she started
talking she mentioned a book she'd been reading called… *The Year of
Yes*. I'm a big believer in synchronicity and I just had to laugh. My
response to her was "I've just opened up my Google doc starting
my chapter on The Power of No!" So here we go…

*"The oldest, shortest words – 'yes' and 'no' – are those
which require the most thought."* – Pythagoras

AUGUST 2

REMEMBER YOUR TIME IS SUPER VALUABLE. IF YOU JUST HAD ONE HOUR TODAY WOULD YOU RATHER A) SPEND TIME HAVING A COFFEE WITH A FRIEND OR B) DOING SOMETHING YOU DON'T WANT TO DO! THIS IS PERSONAL TO YOU. SO JUST FEEL INTO IT. THERE ARE NO WRONG OR RIGHT ANSWERS.

Write a list of the types of things people often ask you that you really would rather say no to. Identify the things that really make your skin itch.

_____

_____

_____

_____

_____

Lisa's musing

Do not worry one bit. I have had to learn this over the years and
I so often still don't get it right. In the moment, when put on the
spot (being the people pleaser I am) it's so easy to just say "yes."
But now I really try to pause and think, and often buy myself time
to really feel into it. I do this with simple phrases like "let me check," or
"let me come back to you." I always do get back to people and
I try not to feel guilty (that's a work in progress).

"Real freedom is saying 'no' without giving a reason." – Amit Kalantri

TODAY WHEN SOMEONE ASKS YOU TO DO SOMETHING, DON'T SAY AN IMMEDIATE "YES" AND LATER REGRET IT. INSTEAD, STOP AND PAUSE. TAKE A BREATH. THEN CHANGE YOUR WORDING TO BUY YOU TIME AND SAY "LET ME GET BACK TO YOU" OR "LET ME CHECK". IT'S TIME TO TAKE BACK CONTROL OF YOUR TIME. THEN, IF IT FEELS RIGHT, SAY YES.

What do you feel when you say no?

_____

_____

_____

_____

Lisa's Musing

Here is an example. This morning I met an acquaintance for a coffee and I loved every minute of it. There was a good energy exchange, until about 40 minutes in when they asked me to help them with something that was very business oriented and something I get paid a lot of money to do. I could feel my energy drop. So I took a breath and said firmly "if you want to chat about that ping me an email with exactly what it is and I'll have one of my team get back to you." Firm. Boundaries. There is a time and a place. When people start pulling at me or wanting something under the guise of a 'friendly catch-up,' it's time to take back control.

"Half of the troubles of this life can be traced to saying yes too quickly and not saying no soon enough." – Josh Billings

AUGUST 4

WHEN GETTING BACK TO PEOPLE AND SAYING NO, IT CAN SEEM OUT OF CHARACTER OR TOO HARSH JUST TO SAY NO OUTRIGHT. SO PRACTICE SAYING IT IN A SOFTER WAY. TRY "I'M NOT COMFORTABLE WITH THAT," "I'D PREFER NOT," OR "I'D RATHER DO..."

Write down all the ways that you feel comfortable saying no.

_____

_____

_____

_____

_____

_____

Lisa's Musing

Recently I was asked to do a campaign for a razor brand. I'm sure it was a great brand, but the alignment wasn't right and that partnership immediately felt off-kilter for me. So, straight up, rather than beat around the bush, I said "Thank you; it just doesn't feel like the right fit for me personally, but I really appreciate you thinking of me."

"I am thankful for all of those who said no to me. It's because of them I'm doing it myself." – Albert Einstein

AUGUST 5

TODAY WE'RE TALKING TRIGGERS. ARE THERE CERTAIN PEOPLE WHO CONSTANTLY ASK FOR FAVOURS OR BLOCKS OF YOUR TIME? LET'S EXPLORE WHY YOU MIGHT FIND IT HARD TO SAY NO TO THEM.

Write down a list of all the people you find it hard to say no to and why:

_____

_____

_____

_____

_____

_____

Lisa's musing

Oh, I have a few of these for sure. Some of them have just been the most extraordinary people to me through my life and I'd do anything for them, but also at what cost? I need to be supportive, but also aware of my own needs. Then there are people who just keep pulling at me from every angle until they wear me down. I end up giving in and then kicking myself. So I'm working on my list, while you work on yours.

"When you say yes to others, make sure you are not saying no to yourself." – Paulo Coelho

WE DEAL WITH STRESS ON A DAILY BASIS, AND SOMETIMES WE DON'T REALISE HOW IT AFFECTS US. TODAY, KEEP A LIST OF ALL (AND I MEAN ALL) THE THINGS THAT STRESSED YOU OUT – EVEN IF IT JUST MADE YOUR HEART TENSE FOR A MOMENT. YOU MIGHT BE SURPRISED HOW LONG YOUR LIST IS.

List your stressors below, and at the end of the day cross out anything that you really didn't need to worry about!

If you need more space, transfer this list to a journal or a spare sheet of paper.

Lisa's musing

Here are mine for today… Some are ridiculous, some are bigger. My coffee order was wrong (I go to the same place most mornings so I felt irritated). My partner niggled at me over and over again about something petty until I flipped, then I felt bad immediately. I thought about getting old and my own mortality. I realised I'd made a big blunder with our storage facilities and miscalculated how much it was going to cost. It threw out my forecasts, budgets and cash flow. Don't get caught up in the stress, instead think about how we can mindset flip and draw on tools to turn this stress around.

Lavender is a great essential oil to reduce stress.

TAKE A LOOK AT YOUR CALENDAR FOR THIS WEEK. HOW MANY MEETINGS, COFFEE CATCH-UPS OR COMMITMENTS DO YOU HAVE SCHEDULED? MEETINGS CAN BE COUNTERPRODUCTIVE AND UNNECESSARY IF THEY AREN'T WITH THE RIGHT PEOPLE, DISCUSSING THE RIGHT TOPICS.

List the meetings/events you have this week. Circle the ones you don't need to attend and underline the ones that are essential:

Lisa's Musing

You might be like me: months in advance I see a clear diary, and so in the past (and sometimes still) I'd say yes to loads of stuff (because it's ages away), but as the time creeps up, I reclaim my diary. I look at what might have made sense at the time, but just isn't a priority now. Don't feel bad about reclaiming your life and your time. Just do it with integrity and kindness.

"Freedom comes when you learn to let go, creation comes when you learn to say no." – Madonna

BOUNDARIES #1
WHAT IS OKAY AND WHAT IS NOT OKAY? TODAY, WRITE A LIST OF YOUR BOUNDARIES AND NON-NEGOTIABLES AROUND YOUR HEALTH.

We'd love to see your list! Share with us at #collectivehub
or post it to our Facebook group: Collective Hub Club.

liza's musing

Boundaries are so important. An absolute non-negotiable for me is around alcohol. I have a ritual where I turn wine glasses upside down in front of me in a restaurant. I've been sober since 8 Nov 2004. There are little rituals and boundaries that empower me around this.

Check out **thewayward.co** for astrology and wellness advice.

BOUNDARIES #2
**TODAY WE WANT YOU TO THINK ABOUT YOUR PERSONAL BOUNDARIES
WHEN IT COMES TO THE OTHER PEOPLE IN YOUR LIFE.**

Use the below space to consider the state of your relationships:

_____

_____

_____

_____

_____

_____

_____

_____

In my personal romantic relationship we help each other to grow as
individuals and as a couple. Boundaries around anything that doesn't
allow us to be our best selves or negative talk towards one another.

Need a little help with your relationship? Try **relationships.org.au**.

BOUNDARIES #3
WE SPEND HUGE AMOUNTS OF OUR LIVES WORKING, SO IT MAKES SENSE TO CREATE SOME GROUND RULES ABOUT OUR WORK/LIFE BALANCE.

Write a list of your boundaries and non-negotiables around your work.

I don't have meetings before 10am, unless it's an absolute imperative. Trust me, people try – and I hold fast. My evenings and my weekends are pretty much off-limits for work meetings too, unless it's something I really want to do.

Collective Hub has a tonne of info about this: **collectivehub.com**.

AUGUST 11

DON'T FOLLOW THE STATUS QUO. JUST BECAUSE EVERYONE ELSE IS SAYING YES, IS THAT ANY REASON TO?

Today, write a list of times you've followed along and in hindsight wish you hadn't. What did you learn? What would you do differently in future?

_____

_____

_____

_____

Lisa's Musing

I remember when everyone was posting black-and-white selfies. A few celebrity friends of mine, who I trust and respect, asked me to post, so in the moment I went along with it. But something didn't sit right as I watched this wave of black-and-white selfies consume our feeds. And so I stopped. Quickly. And I questioned it. I Googled why, got informed, and then wrote a piece on my Insta grid to let people know the reasoning behind it. Don't be afraid to buck the trend, to question everything.

"People think focus means saying yes to the thing you've got to focus on. But that's not what it means at all. It means saying no to the hundred other good ideas that there are. You have to pick carefully. I'm actually as proud of the things we haven't done as the things I have done. Innovation is saying no to 1,000 things." – Steve Jobs

**YOUR GUT, INTUITION – CALL IT WHAT YOU WILL – IS RARELY WRONG.
SO STOP. THINK. TAKE YOUR TIME. TODAY, BEFORE MAKING ANY DECISIONS,
TAKE A MOMENT TO CHECK IN WITH HOW YOU ARE REALLY FEELING.**

Have you made any really great decisions acting on gut instinct?
List them below and read over this page whenever you need the
confidence that you're making the right decisions.

Lisa's Musing

I know every single time I've felt in my gut that something was wrong,
or a bit off, or that I should have said no, it comes back to bite me.

Interesting articles on intuition can be found at **psychologytoday.com**.

YOU NOW KNOW HOW TO SAY NO AND YOU KNOW HOW TO DO IT ASSERTIVELY. SO TODAY YOU'RE ALLOWED TO NEGOTIATE. IT MIGHT GO LIKE THIS: "YES I'LL DO X FOR YOU, IF YOU DO Y FOR ME." THAT WAY IT FEELS MORE EQUAL, MORE ACCOMMODATING, AND THERE IS LESS REASON FOR YOU TO FEEL USED OR RESENTFUL. IT'S A WIN EITHER WAY.

Things I can negotiate today and this week:

_____

_____

_____

_____

_____

_____

Lisa's Musing

I love this one and it's one I use a bit now. It's a way of always saying yes, but on your terms. I call it a 'value exchange' for mutual benefit.

〜〜〜〜〜

"If you need something from somebody always give that person a way to hand it to you." – Sue Monk Kidd

TODAY, MAKE A LIST OF PESKY PEOPLE WHO 'FAKE FRIEND' YOU FOR WHAT YOU CAN DO FOR THEM, RATHER THAN BECAUSE THEY LIKE YOU. THIS IS A VERY CATHARTIC EXERCISE. YOU CAN THEN FIND A WAY TO RID YOURSELF ENERGETICALLY BY SCRUNCHING THE PIECE OF PAPER UP AND THROWING IT IN THE BIN OR POPPING IT IN A BOX IN THE FREEZER (OKAY, IT MIGHT SOUND A BIT WOO-WOO, BUT IT WORKS!).

Use the space below to plan out how you will dispose of your list. Remember to really be mindful of your actions while you're doing them.

_____

_____

_____

_____

Lisa's musing

When *Collective Hub* was at its peak, I had a lot of 'friends', and I learnt to pick them pretty quickly. The ones who actually liked me for me, and loved, appreciated and respected what we were doing, and the ones who just wanted what we could do for them.

We love this article from SocialPro about fake friends:
socialpronow.com/blog/fake-friends.

AUGUST 15

STOP APOLOGISING WHEN YOU SAY NO. TODAY WHEN YOU SAY NO, MEAN IT. DON'T SAY "I DON'T THINK SO" OR "MAYBE". JUST SAY IT. NO MEANS NO.

You can find a polite alternative if it makes you feel better. Practice
a few of these and have them ready to use as soon as you need. Write
down a couple of them below to help you when the time comes.

_____

_____

_____

_____

_____

Lisa's Musing

Be assertive. If someone doesn't take no for an answer and persists,
don't be afraid to stand your ground. When I gave up drinking more
than 16 years ago, people used to say to me a lot, "go on, have a drink."
As soon as I said very firmly, with emphatic energy, "No, thank you,
I don't drink," end of story. No one, not once in 16 years, has pushed
me on it, because I own the decision. I stand by it and I guess people
can feel the decisiveness and firmness behind it.

*"The most common way people give up their power
is by thinking they don't have any."* – Alice Walker

DON'T CHANGE YOUR PLANS AT ALL TODAY. HOW DID YOU PICTURE TODAY GOING WHEN YOU WOKE UP? SAY NO TO ANYTHING THAT INTERFERES WITH THAT PLAN AND SEE HOW MUCH YOU GET DONE.

Things I said no to today:

_____   _____   _____

_____   _____   _____

_____   _____   _____

_____   _____   _____

Lisa's musing

When there are other people in our life, we may have the ideal picture of the perfect day and they decide it's completely different. Sometimes I'm in the mood for going with the flow, other times not. So today I planned to do personal training at 8am down by the beach, go for a coffee and read the papers, come home and write this book for three to four hours. Then go for a massage and a lovely vegan meal tonight. Tick to PT. Tick to coffee and papers. And then my partner wanted to go for a big drive to see some friends, who live an hour away. Sometimes I would, but today I stuck to my guns and just went with my plan. And it feels delicious.

Share your to-do list with family, including shopping lists and family tasks, using **rememberthemilk.com**.

AUGUST 17

SAY NO TO ALCOHOL OR COFFEE (OR WHATEVER YOUR PERSONAL VICE HAPPENS TO BE). WRITE DOWN WHY YOU LOVE YOUR VICE AND HOW YOU FELT NOT HAVING IT TODAY.

My vices are:

I like them because:

Lisa's musing

As you have previously read, I ditched booze in every way, shape and form in 2004, so I'm over 16 years sober as we go to print on this book. I only took up drinking coffee about five years ago… so that's one I'm working on. I don't have many vices (oh, okay hot chips. Love them. All that salt and fat! I'll work on that this week).

Hello Sunday Morning (**hellosundaymorning.org**) is full of information and inspiration for reducing your drinking.

IF YOU LOVE TV, YOU'LL KNOW THAT YOU CAN EASILY GET SUCKED INTO WATCHING HOURS OF IT. TODAY, SAY NO TO ALL TV AND MOVIES... THAT INCLUDES WATCHING THEM ON IPADS AND LAPTOPS!

Make a list of what you will do instead tonight.

_____

_____

_____

_____

_____

_____

Lisa's musing

You know what? I'm so over TV lately. Remember back in the day when you would walk to the video store and pick one for a decadent night in? If it was crap that was your one choice and you just curled up and were in for the ride. These days there is just too much choice. I can waste hours flicking through what to watch and never actually get anywhere. So, for now, I'm out entirely.

Search **fastcompany.com** for an article titled *How Giving Up TV For A Month Changed My Brain And My Life.*

OUR OWN GOALS CAN GET SIDELINED BY SAYING YES TOO MUCH.

Write down what you would like to achieve this week. Then fill in all
the things you can and need to say no to, to make this happen.

_____

_____

_____

_____

_____

_____

_____

Liza's Musing

You may know by now that I always have an A4 and an A5 notepad
with me. At the start of each month I write down the 10 things I want
to achieve that month across all aspects of my life in the A4 notepad.
They are specific and measurable. Then each day on my A5 pad I write
down my specific tactical to-do list to get them done. If things get in
the way of them getting done, it has to be a no.

Find beautiful journals at *Collective Hub* and **notely.com.au**.

TAKE A MOMENT TODAY TO UNDERSTAND WHERE YOUR PRIORITIES LIE.

Answer these questions:

How do you like to spend your free time?

What do you wish you had more time for?

What do you have in your life that makes it wonderful?

What should you say no to?

Lisa's Musing

Such a beautiful exercise. I hope this one leaves you radiating and ready to step forward with positivity, determination and strength. Let's go.

A helpful article for this can be found at:
success.com/6-steps-to-discover-your-true-self.

SAY NO TO NEGATIVE TALK TODAY. WOMEN TEND TO PLAY THEMSELVES DOWN AND EVEN BULLY OURSELVES SOMETIMES WITHOUT REALISING IT. TODAY, WHEN YOU FEEL THE URGE TO FEEL GUILTY OR FEEL LIKE YOU'RE NOT DOING ENOUGH, STOP AND REFRAME YOUR THINKING.

Write down five compliments about yourself.

1. _____

2. _____

3. _____

4. _____

5. _____

Lisa's musing

Even tongue-in-cheek. My PT put a little Insta story up recently of me doing a stair run. I reposted it with the self-deprecating caption: "more like a little Oompa Loompa than Wonder Woman." But you know what? That was 50 mins into training and six stair sprints into that one set of stairs. We are so harsh on ourselves and our own worst critics. Let's be kind and loving to ourselves. I am strong. I am proud. I turned up. And I did better than yesterday. And I feel great.

Butterfly Foundation can help if you need to rethink the way you talk about yourself: **butterfly.org.au**.

TRY SOMETHING DIFFERENT. WHEN SOMEONE ASKS FOR SOMETHING, RATHER THAN SAYING "NO", I WANT YOU TO INSTEAD SAY "YES, BUT..."

Situations when I could say "yes, but..." today or this week are:

_____

_____

_____

_____

Lisa's musing

Let me explain. This is about taking power back. You can always do this, because you have control over the 'but'. Someone asked me recently "Can I pick your brains and ask you about publishing?" (My least fave statement btw: pick your brains. Loathe it). Rather than an outright no, I reframed it and thought about an equal and fair value exchange. Then I said "Yes, but if you match me for the hour of my time with an hour of yours teaching me how to build an app." See how I changed the game on this one? Practice it today. It's fun because you can literally say "yes, but..." then anything you want.

"No is a complete sentence. It does not require an explanation to follow. You can truly answer someone's request with a simple no." – Sharon E. Rainey

TODAY, PRACTICE SAYING NO WITHOUT GIVING A REASON

What are some of the things people might request of you today?
Will you have the confidence to say no without an explanation? List some
strategies below to help you achieve today's exercise - it won't be easy!

_____

_____

_____

_____

_____

_____

_____

Lisa's Musing

How hard was that? This is absolutely not easy. Today's
exercise is really tough, because we often feel like we need
to justify our answer. Today, just own it. I dare you.

YouTube is a fantastic resource for this – search "how to say no".

AUGUST 24

TODAY, CONSIDER THE OPPORTUNITY/COST OF SAYING YES TO EVERYTHING.

Then write down how each yes made you feel. Were there any times you really wanted to say no? Do you value your ability to say no now?

_____

_____

_____

_____

_____

Lisa's Musing

I'm starting to push and test you now. You've had 23 days to get your practice on. I want you to start to feel the ick that comes with a yes when you mean no. It's good for you to feel that again now you have come so far and are feeling (I'm sure) so strong. I did it today all day, just to test how it felt, and now – yuck! I have to go and reverse seven lots of yes! Wish me luck.

For help understanding the effects of today,
search "self sabotage" at **naturalhealthmag.com.au**.

NOW THAT YOU'VE GOT THIS FAR, HOW DO YOU FEEL ABOUT THE WORD NO?

Answer these questions: Do you feel it's taboo? Do you feel comfortable? Do you feel confident? Do you feel better saying no and having boundaries?

Today, really feel into what the past 24 days have made you feel. What were the lessons? What will you take forward?

_____

_____

_____

_____

_____

Lisa's Musing

I feel empowered. As I've been writing this chapter it's pushed me to really feel much more consciously into the power of no. I feel taller, stronger, more aligned and confident. It's actually a gift. So, thank you for reading. I'm really enjoying going on this journey again.

"It takes true courage and real humility to say no or yes."

– Ernest Agyemang Yeboah

SEPARATE REFUSAL FROM REJECTION. REMEMBER, YOU ARE TURNING DOWN A REQUEST, NOT AN ACTUAL PERSON.

Can you think of a time when you took a refusal as rejection?

How did it make you feel?

Were you right to feel that way?

Lisa's Musing

This is tricky, right? When someone says to me "it's not personal," it generally gets my back up and my immediate reaction is "yes, it is." That's my ego. So I wind back and think maybe my request was unreasonable. Or maybe it was reasonable for me, but not the right timing or alignment for them. We never quite know what's going on in someone else's world, and everyone has the right to say no. It's not ours to question why. Just accept.

Understand your triggers and reactions at **justsayno.com**.

CONSIDER A COMPROMISE. HERE'S ANOTHER WAY OF THINKING ABOUT THIS: TODAY, RESPOND TO REQUESTS BY THINKING ABOUT A COMPROMISE. SO NOT A FLAT OUT NO, AND NOT A YES. REALLY FEEL INTO IT AND LAND SOMEWHERE IN BETWEEN.

When have you compromised in your life and it turned out really well?

Is there a time when you compromised and it didn't work for you?

What could you have done differently?

Lisa's Musing

I really believe in value exchange in life. Equal energy exchanges. It could be around helping someone, or a monetary exchange, but today I want you to focus on an equal energetic exchange. Now this might be contrary to what you are thinking, you might really want to help someone and you are actually getting more out of it than they are. So just feel through whatever feels right for you. Where is the compromise to land here?

Improve your direct language with the Just Not Sorry Gmail plugin. It'll help you say what you really mean.

KNOW DEEP WITHIN YOU THAT SAYING NO DOESN'T MAKE YOU A BAD PERSON

Think about a time that you said no to a situation or person and felt bad about it. Now what would you say to a friend who went through the same thing? Would you want them to feel bad about it?

_____

_____

_____

_____

_____

_____

_____

Lisa's musing

Feel into that. Sit with it. Repeat it: "Saying no does not make me a bad person." I want you to really get that today.

〜〜〜〜

"When you say no to the wrong people, it opens up the space for the right people to come in." – Joe Calloway

TRULY UNDERSTAND YOUR VALUE THAT YOU BRING TO INDIVIDUALS, YOUR COMMUNITY AND THE WORLD TODAY.

Use the space below to really unpack what you love about yourself, what you're good at, what others love about you and what they say you're good at. You might just surprise yourself at how much value you bring to the world.

Liza's Musing

Don't underestimate yourself. Everyone has value. Everyone!

〜〜〜〜

"Success seems to be connected with action. Successful people keep moving. They make mistakes, but they don't quit." – Conrad Hilton

BE TRUE TO YOURSELF. THAT IS ALL. YOU'VE DONE GREAT THROUGH THIS CHAPTER. TODAY, LET'S CELEBRATE YOUR PROGRESS THIS MONTH.

What are three lessons you learned from this month of saying no?

In what circumstances will you use them?

Lisa's Musing

In 2004 I did a course called The Hoffman Process. I went in one person. I came out another. I learned to let go of the expectation of others and living life according to other people's hopes and dreams. I got a true semblance of who I was, what my values and beliefs were. And that was the beginning of my spiritual and wellness journey, and pursuing a life of learning, seeking and getting really clear and comfortable with who I am. Much of that journey has been about saying no and standing up for myself.

Instead of having to say the word no, install the Just Say No button on your phone and press it any time you need the word "no" as a response. Ha ha!

AUGUST 31

WRITE DOWN ALL THE THINGS YOU CAN CONTROL IN YOUR LIFE (SOCIAL LIFE, WORK, HOW YOU APPROACH YOUR HEALTH, FRIENDSHIPS), AND ALL THE THINGS YOU DON'T HAVE CONTROL OVER (YOUR BOSS, TAXES, GLOBAL ISSUES, FAMILY COMMITMENTS). THEN COMMIT TO SAYING NO FROM NOW ON TO ANYTHING YOU DON'T WANT TO DO. YOU'VE HAD A MONTH OF PRACTICE, SO NOW IT'S TIME TO USE YOUR NEW SKILLS!

My commitment to myself:

Lisa's musing

One of my favourite sayings is the Serenity Prayer: "God, grant me the serenity to accept the things I cannot change, courage to change the things I can, and wisdom to know the difference." Take this with you into today and for the next month. Now a massive well done! I'm so proud of you. Whoever you are. Wherever you are. We are all in this together. Just imagine as we all see the same sun and the same moon wherever we are, there will be thousands and thousands of people reading this journey and going along in sync with you. There is power in that.

Search 'How to Say No' on grammarly.com for inspo.

september

ENCOURAGE PRODUCTIVITY

Finding (and keeping) your motivation throughout the year can be challenging, especially if you're being pulled in every direction. Your to-do list keeps growing, your patience keeps shrinking, and you just don't feel like logging on each day.

We hear ya! We've definitely been there. But don't worry! This month we'll be sharing our best and most effective productivity hacks, tips and tricks to get you (and keep you) on track.

Each day you'll find activities to help you prioritise and structure your to-do list, encourage your creative mojo to flow, and help you reach your goals. Whatever they may be. By the end of it, you'll be an efficiency expert, ready to take on whatever life throws at you.

So, gather up all those things you've been meaning to do, and let's find a way to get them scratched off your to-do list!

CHOOSE YOUR FIVE MOTIVATING WORDS FOR THIS MONTH: THEY COULD BE STRATEGIC, ORGANISED, COLLABORATIVE, CREATIVE, POSITIVE - WHATEVER MAKES YOU FEEL STRONG AND CONFIDENT.

Use the space below to write your five words and then explain why you chose them. Then write them on another piece of paper and put them on your desk or on the fridge so you can focus on them each morning. If you're up to it, share them with us! #collectivehub or post in our Facebook group (Collective Hub Club) so we can all feel motivated together.

1. _____   _____

2. _____   _____

3. _____   _____

4. _____   _____

5. _____   _____

Lisa's Musing

These are the words that will drive, motivate and keep us on track this month. Whenever you start to feel a bit wobbly or lose focus, look at them. This is a simple but powerful ritual. Trust me. It works.

"Productivity is never an accident. It is always the result of a commitment to excellence, intelligent planning, and focussed effort." – Paul J. Meyer

WHAT LIMITS YOUR PRODUCTIVITY? IS IT STRESS? FAMILY? TIME? ARE THEY FACTORS OUT OF YOUR CONTROL? CAN YOU FIND STRATEGIES TO OVERCOME THEM? DON'T JUST FOCUS ON THE PROBLEM BUT ALSO THE SOLUTION.

Take time today to write a list of the times you feel most productive, and the times you don't.

Times I feel most productive:

_____

_____

_____

Times I don't feel productive:

_____

_____

_____

Lisa's Musing

For me, I like big chunks of uninterrupted quiet space and it really depends on the project I'm working on. So I ensure I set myself up in the best possible surroundings to give myself the amount of time I need to get through that task. I've become good at shutting out noise and being able to focus inwardly. I try to structure my day so that I have chunks of time to get through each project. For example, at the time of writing this musing, I've been here for four hours straight. It is Saturday and I allowed myself one 15-minute break to go and get a coffee.

Find lots of great content about this at **developgoodhabits.com**.

RESEARCH A SUCCESSFUL LEADER YOU ADMIRE. IT COULD BE SOMEONE FROM WITHIN YOUR INDUSTRY, SOMEONE WHO HAS A BIG PROFILE, OR EVEN A MENTOR OR A COLLEAGUE OF YOURS.

Answer these questions about them: How did they become successful? What were their mistakes and what lessons do they share about them? What drives them, and what is it that sets them apart? Now have a brainstorm about how they would approach the limitations you wrote about yesterday.

Lisa's Musing

This is such an incredible way to lift beyond your perceived limitations. I often remind myself of this one simple thing: we all have the exact same amount of hours in the day as everyone else. Let's hone our mindset and skills and use them wisely. And remember, success leaves clues, so watch and learn.

"Do it now. You become more successful the moment you start moving towards a worthwhile goal." – Samuel Johnson

DELEGATE: YOU'RE ONLY ONE PERSON. CAN YOU DELEGATE A WORK PROJECT, THE COOKING OF A MEAL, A PHONE CALL?

Write down three tasks you could outsource, then explain why you haven't done so already.

1. _____

_____

2. _____

_____

3. _____

_____

Liza's Musing

I have written tomes on this stuff! When I started my first business, I used to try to do everything. Now I call in experts for every aspect of my life: business, health, home. The lot. I use my time to focus on what I love, what keeps me well, where I can be of greatest service and what is (in the case of business) the most rewarding and commercially viable.

An article we loved about delegating can be found here: **meistertask.com/blog/delegate-tasks-effectively**.

DOING WORK THAT MOTIVATES YOU WILL MEAN YOU ARE NATURALLY MORE PRODUCTIVE. SO LET'S FIND OUT WHAT'S IMPORTANT TO YOU.

Where do you want to be three months, one year and five years from now?

Three months:

One year:

Five years:

Lisa's Musing

Ask yourself these simple questions: What do I love and makes me want to jump out of bed every morning? What makes me feel alive? What makes me excited and energised? If your work isn't doing these things for you then it might be time to reconsider, pivot, change, adapt, outsource more of what you don't like. Just be courageous enough to keep aligning to what makes you happy.

"Without leaps of imagination or dreaming, we lose the excitement of possibilities. Dreaming, after all, is a form of planning." – Gloria Steinem

BE PURPOSEFULLY COUNTERINTUITIVE. THIS IS A GREAT EXERCISE TO TRICK YOUR BRAIN OUT OF ITS NORMAL PATTERNS. START TO DO THINGS EVERY DAY THAT ARE COUNTERINTUITIVE TO YOUR ROUTINE. IF YOU WALK A CERTAIN WAY TO WORK, GO A DIFFERENT ROUTE. SWITCH UP YOUR COFFEE ORDER. MAKING THESE CHANGES WILL EMPOWER YOU TO BE MORE ASSERTIVE, DIRECT AND DECISIVE ABOUT WHAT YOU WANT TO ACHIEVE.

Write or scribble down every counterintuitive act you were able
to perform today. How did each one make you feel?

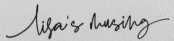

I started doing this in 2004 when I truly started working consciously on myself. I knew that to become the best version of myself I needed to stop doing things the way they'd always been done. It was about simple baby steps to train my brain. These days, I constantly flip just about anything and keep life fresh all the time.

The Productive – Habit Tracker app can help streamline your life.

WHEN IS YOUR PRODUCTIVITY MOMENTUM THE HIGHEST? TO FIND OUT, PLAN THREE IMPORTANT TASKS FOR TODAY – ONE FOR THE MORNING, ONE FOR THE AFTERNOON AND ONE FOR THE EVENING.

Track your tasks in the spaces below. At the end of the day, compare your productivity for the different times and then reflect on your day!

Morning:

Afternoon:

Evening:

_____

_____

_____

Reflection:

_____

_____

_____

Lisa's musing

Don't worry what your answer is. My partner gets up at 3.59am every morning. He loves it and is super productive before his team starts work at 8am, four hours later. I, on the other hand, am not a morning person. I actually work best in the evenings. So find out what works for you and be unashamed about it. You do you.

∿∿∿

Some great organisational apps are Any.do and Todoist.

BATCH YOUR TASKS: DO ALL YOUR BILLS AT ONCE, REPLY TO ALL YOUR VOICEMAILS AT ONCE, AND IRON ALL THOSE CLEAN CLOTHES AT ONCE. IT SAVES ALL KINDS OF TIME.

Looking at your to-do list, write down three ways you could batch your tasks. Is there a particular time you could do each one? Would you delegate any?

1. _____

_____

2. _____

_____

3. _____

_____

Lisa's Musing

Oh, all the tedious stuff and the minutiae of life that most of us really do not enjoy (except maybe the detail-oriented organisers among us… if that's you, I need you!). Batching them and just going at them first thing in the morning gets them out of the way, they don't hang over us like a dark cloud and we can then get on with what we really love doing. And anything that you don't love and can outsource – I say, do it!

～～～～～

Create your own customisable organiser with **mementodatabase.com**.

GET UP EARLY TODAY BEFORE ANYONE ELSE IN THE HOUSE. JUST HALF AN HOUR TO YOURSELF WILL MEAN YOU CAN FINISH SOMETHING YOU'VE BEEN PUTTING OFF AND CROSS IT OFF YOUR TO-DO LIST.

Write an early-morning to-do list for today. Check off every one you managed to do. Then list three words that describe your morning.

Lisa's Musing

I've already said I'm not a morning person, but when I do get up early, it is quite extraordinary how many more hours there are in the day. And I surprise myself with how much I've done even by 9am sometimes! I was staying at my mother-in-law's in Sydney's northern suburbs a few nights ago. I woke up at 5.45am to a cacophony of extraordinary sounds of frogs, birds chirping and all sorts of other wonders I wouldn't normally hear. It set me up for the most amazing day. Also, I've now started doing soft sand running at 5.45am twice a week!

"Have a bias towards action – let's see something happen now. You can break that big plan into small steps and take the first step right away." – Indira Gandhi

SEPTEMBER 10

TO REALLY POWER THROUGH TODAY, FIND A PLACE AWAY FROM DISTRACTION AND LISTEN TO SLOWER-PACED INSTRUMENTAL MUSIC OR NATURE SOUNDS TO HELP YOU REALLY FOCUS.

Write down your to-do list here, in order of priority.

_____

_____

_____

_____

_____

_____

Lisa's musing

Easier said than done sometimes. Especially if we have a year like 2020 in which so many people found themselves working from home – kids, parents, laptops, everyone piled into one living room trying to be productive. Last chapter was the power of "no"… so let's build on that and get strong on being unafraid to have boundaries and find some quiet space just for you.

Spotify has some great 'focus' and 'studying' playlists, which I love to use when I have a tonne of work to get through!

**RESEARCH FIVE APPS THAT WILL HELP YOU WITH PRODUCTIVITY
- THINK OUT OF THE BOX. PERHAPS ONE COULD BE A MEDITATION APP,
OR AN APP THAT HELPS YOU FALL ASLEEP FASTER.**

Write down each app and how you will use it to help you
be more productive and efficient with your time.

_____

_____

_____

_____

_____

Lisa's Musing

Since I decentralised my team after 17 years in a bricks-and-mortar office, I've become very tech-savvy and rely heavily on all sorts of apps and software to help us run an efficient, productive, streamlined team. Find whatever it is that works for you. We use Asana, Google Docs, Dropbox, Xero and Zoom for software, and to message each other and keep on top of communication we use WhatsApp, Slack, Todoist, Evernote.

Freedom app allows you to block the websites that most distract you on your smartphone and computer in order to help you focus.

USE THE 'ONE SCREEN ONLY' RULE TODAY AND MAKE SURE YOU'RE ONLY CONNECTED TO ONE SCREEN AT A TIME – NO SCROLLING DURING TV SHOWS, OR WORKING ON YOUR LAPTOP WHILE FLICKING THROUGH YOUR TABLET.

Use the space below to reflect on your productivity using this strategy.

_____

_____

_____

_____

_____

_____

_____

lisa's musing

I have an extraordinary screen from HP that enables me to have three screens open at once for when I go into standing desk, super-productive mode. I often switch between email, web pages and a doc I'm working on simultaneously if I really need to have multiple screens open at once.

"Technology should improve your life… not become your life." – Billy Cox

IT'S TIME FOR EXERCISE! EVEN JUST A QUICK WORKOUT CAN BOOST YOUR PRODUCTIVITY. SO TODAY, FOR EVERY HOUR YOU WORK, STOP AND DO A QUICK BURST OF EXERCISES TO KEEP YOU MOTIVATED.

Use this page to plan your workouts. Choose from actions like stair sprints, five burpees, 10 push-ups, 15 sit-ups, walking around the block. Note down the time you did them and check them off the list as you do them.

_____

_____

_____

_____

_____

_____

Lisa's Musing

Truly there are so many simple exercises you can do right next to your office chair (or wherever you are working from). No excuses, people. Let's go!

～～～～～

Try the 7-Minute Workout app for ideas.

DID YOU KNOW A US STUDY FOUND THAT, ON AVERAGE, PEOPLE TOUCH THEIR PHONES 2,617 TIMES A DAY? SO TODAY LET'S BLOCK SOCIAL MEDIA USE. DECIDE HOW LONG YOU WILL ALLOW YOURSELF TO CHECK IN, AND AT WHAT TIME. NOTE HOW THIS AFFECTS YOUR PRODUCTIVITY.

Commit to the time and length of your social media access today. Use the space below to create limitations and boundaries on your device use.

lisa's musing

Does anyone else have one of those little timers that pops up to remind you how much time you've spent on your device? If you don't, might be time to get one...

Apps to help curb/monitor social media usage include Appdetox, Forest and Offtime.

SEPTEMBER 15

DISTRACTIONS ARE THE ENEMY OF PRODUCTIVITY. USE THIS PAGE TODAY TO WRITE DOWN ANY OFF-TOPIC THOUGHTS, IDEAS OR NOTES THAT COME TO YOU WHILE YOU'RE TRYING TO WORK.

Circle any ideas you think are worth actioning.

Lisa's Musing

If you are a procrastinator, even if you can't stand vacuuming, suddenly the idea of racing around the house cleaning becomes your best friend so you can avoid what really needs to be done. Stop! You need to remember what you are trying to achieve and why. Then work out what is blocking you and how to overcome it.

"Our goals can only be reached through a vehicle of a plan, in which we must fervently believe, and upon which we must vigorously act. There is no other route to success." – Pablo Picasso

WEAR HEADPHONES: EVEN IF YOU'RE JUST LISTENING TO WHITE NOISE. YOU'LL BE AMAZED HOW MUCH MORE WORK YOU'LL BE ABLE TO DO.

Write down your five favourite playlists for productivity.
Refer back to this page any time you need to get work done.

1. _____

2. _____

3. _____

4. _____

5. _____

Lisa's musing

A little admission on behalf of my partner: when he's in the office he always wears big headphones. He rarely has anything playing, but it gives the impression that he is not to be interrupted. It works a treat. And I can relate. When I had an office I used to say I was 'busy' but not 'productive'. Everyone was always grabbing me to problem solve, so my day became reactive rather than proactive. If you have headphones on, it empowers the team to get on and find solutions themselves.

If you need background music and want to try something new, search 'My Favourite Coffee Shop' on Spotify. I love it.

WHAT CAN YOU AUTOMATE IN YOUR WORK AND HOME LIFE TO SAVE YOU TIME AND HASSLE? IT COULD BE AS SIMPLE AS SETTING UP AUTOMATED PAYMENTS FOR BILLS, OR PERHAPS IT'S A VIRTUAL ASSISTANT FOR ADMIN.

Write down five tasks that are time or energy consuming.
How can you reduce the time you spend on them?

1. _____

2. _____

3. _____

4. _____

5. _____

Lisa's Musing

There is so much great technology that can help you to streamline,
and there are people who love doing what you don't and vice versa.
So look at what you can outsource and automate.

~~~~~~

Try OfficeLens (converts photos/scans to PDFs),
Sanebox (manages your email notifications/spam for you),
Brill.app (scans your handwritten notes and creates digital files),
Shift (manages all your conversations, tasks across various
social media apps, emails and programs).

TEMPLATES ARE AN EFFECTIVE WAY TO BOOST PRODUCTIVITY. DO YOU SEND THE SAME EMAIL REPLY OUT ALL THE TIME? OR PERHAPS YOU SPEND TIME SEARCHING FOR HASHTAGS OR WRITING COMMENTS. TAKE TIME TODAY TO CRAFT SOME TEMPLATES TO BE USED FROM NOW ON.

Use the space below to list all the tasks you could create a template for:

_____

_____

_____

_____

_____

Lisa's Musing

My team and I have developed so many templates that we use to track daily financials. Each team member has pulse checks. But if you look on **collectivehub.com**, you will see that we've produced loads of journals on almost every topic. They are filled with templates from daily gratitudes to financial P&Ls.

Canva can be a great tool for designing templates and making them look beautiful.

REDUCING THE AMOUNT OF DECISIONS YOU NEED TO MAKE IN A DAY WILL HELP YOU BE MORE EFFECTIVE. WHERE CAN YOU PRE-PLAN? PLANNING A WEEK'S WORTH OF MEALS, OR FIVE DAYS' WORTH OF SOCIAL MEDIA POSTS, WILL SAVE YOU TIME AND STRESS.

Write down three tasks you could pre-plan
this week to help you be more productive.

_____

_____

_____

_____

_____

_____

_____

lisa's musing

Check out **planoly.com** to help you plan your social media,
and there are heaps other great tools out there, too.

~~~~~~

We love the book *The Fit Foodie Meal Prep Plan*
by Sally O'Neil for food prepping strategies.

TIME FOR SELF-CARE! YES, WE FIT THIS INTO EVERY CHALLENGE. WHY? BECAUSE IT'S SO IMPORTANT FOR MENTAL HEALTH. BOOK A MASSAGE, GO FOR A WALK, WATCH A MOVIE. ANYTHING TO GIVE YOUR BRAIN A BREAK.

Use the space below to draw a picture. Even 10 minutes of doodling can be a great form of self-care!

I hope today gave you a lovely little shock and surprise. Yes, today is a 'you' day. Just you. No need to be productive. Taking a 100 per cent self-care day is going to make you so much more productive. Make sure that you take self-care breaks every day, and every now and then give yourself a complete day off during the week. You'll feel much better for it. And, trust me, some of your greatest ideas will come in these down times… so really it's productive time after all. Go you!

Our favourite app for meal planning is BigOven – it lets you save recipes, make shopping lists and plan a week's worth of food. Brilliant.

LET'S PLAY WITH TIMINGS TODAY. IT MIGHT BE HARD, BUT CHOOSE TWO TIMES TODAY THAT YOU WILL CHECK YOUR EMAIL. ONE IN THE MORNING AND ONE IN THE AFTERNOON. IF THIS DOESN'T WORK FOR YOUR WORK, YOU CAN ADD IN A THIRD SLOT, BUT THE IDEA IS NOT TO GET SIDELINED WITH THE CONSTANT PINGING OF EMAILS IN YOUR INBOX. TO HELP MANAGE OTHER PEOPLE'S EXPECTATIONS, YOU CAN SET UP AN OUT-OF-OFFICE, EXPLAINING WHEN YOU WILL BE AVAILABLE VIA EMAIL.

Times I will be on email today:

_____

_____

_____

_____

_____

_____

Lisa's Musing

Leverage, leverage, leverage. Try it. It makes life so much easier and your brain doesn't have to flip-flop about and multitask in the moment so much.

"Lighten up, just enjoy life, smile more, laugh more, and don't get so worked up about things." – Kenneth Branagh

SEPTEMBER 22

SAY GOODBYE TO PERFECTION. WAITING FOR EVERYTHING TO BE PERFECT WILL KILL YOUR MOTIVATION AND RUIN YOUR MOMENTUM.

Write down any projects or tasks you've been putting off doing because you're waiting for the timing to be perfect, or waiting for a perfect outcome.

_____

_____

_____

_____

_____

_____

_____

Lisa's musing

Done is better than perfect. Just start. Chances are you will iterate and change over and over again. So, you might as well just start!

"If you look for perfection, you'll never be content." – Leo Tolstoy

DON'T IGNORE PROFESSIONAL DEVELOPMENT. WHAT SKILLS WOULD YOU LIKE TO IMPROVE ON? DO SOME RESEARCH AND SIGN UP FOR A COURSE THAT WILL BENEFIT YOU. THIS CAN BE A YOUTUBE TUTORIAL, AN ONLINE COURSE, OR A SHORT COURSE. WHATEVER IT IS, BE REALISTIC WITH YOUR TIME - HOW MUCH STUDY TIME CAN YOU FIT IN EVERY WEEK?

Write a list of the skills you'd like to have and courses you can do to upskill.

_____

_____

_____

_____

_____

Lisa's Musing

Whatever you are using right now as an excuse to self sabotage or not do this – "I'm too old," "I'm too young," "I don't have time," "I can't afford it…" Just stop. Continual learning and development is so important. It keeps us moving forward. It keeps us challenged, invigorated and alive. And it keeps us productive.

General Assembly (**generalassemb.ly**) has a range short courses that are helpful for anyone running their own business or looking to upskill.

FOCUS ON YOUR WORK ENVIRONMENT. WHAT IS YOUR DESK LIKE? NEAT AND ORGANISED, MESSY AND CREATIVE, OR DO YOU WORK AT A LOCAL CAFE?

Use this page to draw your dream office. After you've finished, think about how you could incorporate this dream office into your current workspace.

If you need more space, transfer your drawing to a journal or a spare sheet of paper.

Lisa's Musing

I used to be super-duper messy. Paper everywhere. But now that I'm so mobile, I try to stay as streamlined as possible. Tidy desk, tidy mind. That's my motto now. I print stuff out when I need to really focus and read through it and make notes. But then it's off to the recycling bin. Check out my Instagram @lisamessenger to see my office wall – it's basically my brain on a wall. Pages from all my books and other inspiration I find. It makes me happy and it's all in one place.

Find beautiful stationery to make your work shine at **scratchandjotter.com.au**.

HYDRATE! STUDIES SHOW THAT EVEN TWO PER CENT WATER LOSS CAN AFFECT YOUR COGNITIVE PERFORMANCE. WANT TO BOOST YOUR PRODUCTIVITY? JUST ADD WATER! YOU COULD EVEN TAKE THE TIME TO VISIT A POOL, THE BEACH OR JUST ENJOY A LONG BATH OR SHOWER.

Let's keep a water tally – include all the water you drink, non-caffeinated teas, and juices, and refrain from coffee (sorry!) and caffeinated teas.

Lisa's musing

Drink, drink, drink! H_2O all day, all the way. This does not come naturally to me even though it's been hammered into me all my life. So, let's do this together. I'm going for eight glasses a day!

We love the beautiful water bottles from **aayu.com.au**.

SEPTEMBER 26

WE ALL KNOW SPENDING TIME IN NATURE HAS HUGE BENEFITS FOR OUR WELLBEING, BUT DID YOU KNOW THAT EVEN JUST LOOKING AT GREENERY ON A SCREEN CAN BOOST PRODUCTIVITY? SO, SPEND 10 MINUTES CREATING A PLAYLIST OF NATURE IMAGES AND FLICK THROUGH THESE IMAGES TO BOOST YOUR MOTIVATION TODAY.

Write down some of your favourite nature views - where are they? Who were you with? How did you feel when you looked at each view?

_____

_____

_____

_____

Lisa's Musing

This one I have down pat. I love nature. At last count, I think I have well over 100 plants in and around our home. I love planting, pruning, watching things grow. Smelling it and soaking it up in whatever way I can. It is my lifeblood. It soothes my soul.

~~~~~~~~

This visual playlist can be created on your phone, laptop or Pinterest.

SAY NO TO NETFLIX! TODAY, TURN OFF THE TV FOR THE WHOLE DAY. NO LUNCHTIME OR AFTER-DINNER MOVIES OR BINGE WATCHING YOUR FAVOURITE TV SERIES. INSTEAD, FOCUS ON TREATING YOURSELF TO A LITTLE SELF-CARE. READ YOUR BOOK, LISTEN TO MUSIC, ENJOY YOUR SACRED SPACE, ANYTHING THAT MAKES YOU FEEL GOOD.

Write down here the three ways you will treat yourself today:

1. _____

_____

2. _____

_____

3. _____

_____

Lisa's musing

One of my fave things to do. Find a sunny nook inside or outside. Grab a comfy blanket for comfort and curl up with a good book or magazine. No tech in sight. Delicious.

Have a book specially chosen for you each month with a subscription to **bookabuy.com.au**.

SEPTEMBER 28

WIP YOURSELF! HAVE A TWO-MINUTE WORK-IN-PROGRESS MEETING WITH YOURSELF BEFORE LUNCH. WHAT WILL YOU COMMIT TO FINISHING BEFORE THE DAY IS OUT?

Record your WIP minutes here:

_____

_____

_____

_____

_____

_____

_____

Lisa's Musing

Or, trick yourself into feeling like you've achieved a lot by writing down every item on your to-do list, just so you can tick everything off!

"Good fortune is what happens when opportunity meets with planning." – Thomas Edison

TAKE A COLD SHOWER. YES, REALLY. AS WELL AS THE LONG-TERM HEALTH BENEFITS, STUDIES SHOW THAT COLD SHOWERS BOOST MOOD AND ALERTNESS, WHICH CAN HELP WITH FOCUS AND GOAL-SETTING. START THE DAY WITH A COLD SHOWER AND NOTE DOWN HERE HOW YOU FELT AFTERWARDS. WHAT WILL YOU ACCOMPLISH TODAY?

How did your cold shower feel? Do you feel fresh? Alive?
Use the below space to note how much your productivity changed.

Liza's Musing

I've gotten into a habit of 40 seconds of cold water at the end of every shower. I've also done ice baths in the past (this is not a daily habit!).

Check out **@iceman_hof**, if you want some chilly inspiration.

DON'T GLAMORISE BEING BUSY. THE NEXT TIME SOMEONE ASKS HOW YOU ARE OR IF YOU'RE AVAILABLE, DON'T JUST SAY "I'M BUSY," EXPLAIN WHAT YOU HAVE TO DO INSTEAD. FOR EXAMPLE, "I'D LOVE TO CATCH UP BUT I HAVE A PRESENTATION TO WRITE AND I HAVE A MEETING AT 3PM." THIS WILL LESSEN ANY FEELINGS OF GUILT AND SHOW HOW PRODUCTIVE YOU ARE.

Let's change your language. Use this page to rewrite your goals. For example, "I'm not busy, I'm creating my best life." "I'm not busy, I'm building a business."

_____

_____

_____

_____

_____

Lisa's Musing

Being busy is not the same as being productive. Language is so important, so let's get super conscious about what we say. Does it truly match how we are feeling or want to feel?

"To achieve great things, two things are needed; a plan, and not quite enough time." – Leonard Bernstein

What lessons did you learn this month and what habits will you keep?

_____

_____

_____

_____

_____

_____

_____

_____

_____

_____

_____

_____

_____

_____

october

DECLUTTER YOUR LIFE

Let's look at what's holding you back. It's time to declutter – and we mean *everything*. That's right, we're not just talking about the clutter in your home, this month we're also tackling all the excess 'stuff and things' cluttering up your entire life.

From your Instagram feed to your friends, your book pile to your desktop, we are diving in and clearing out.

Clutter in a metaphorical and a physical sense can start to weigh us down, making us feel anxious and trapped.

But it doesn't have to be that way! In 30 days' time, when you have cleared space in your life for the act of living, you'll feel freer, less stressed and happier.

And I suspect you might even sleep better!

OCTOBER 1

BEFORE WE START THIS MONTH OF DECLUTTERING, LET'S FOCUS ON WHAT IS IMPORTANT TO YOU. ONCE YOU TRULY UNDERSTAND THAT, MAKING DECISIONS ABOUT DECLUTTERING YOUR LIFE WILL BE MUCH EASIER.

Use the below space to write down how you would like others to describe you. We're not talking about the reality of your life, we're talking about the perception of your life. Circle any particularly important statements.

_____

_____

_____

_____

_____

Lisa's Musing

I for one am excited about this month! As I've mentioned before, my natural propensity is not to be clutter-free, but I've learned to be, and I know my life is so much smoother for it. I'd say I'm more a maximalist in every part of life, but am happier when I'm practicing minimalism.

"Clutter is nothing more than postponed decisions." – Barbara Hemphill

LET'S LOOK AT YOUR SELF-WORTH. WE TEND TO HOARD ITEMS WHEN WE FEEL OUR SENSE OF WORTH IS LACKING. SO TODAY, WRITE DOWN 10 THINGS YOU LIKE ABOUT YOURSELF.

Find a mantra that speaks to you about your self worth.
If you're stuck, you can use "I am enough. I always will be enough."

_____

_____

_____

_____

_____

Before I truly stepped into my purpose in 2013, I used to buy a lot of 'stuff'. I used it to fill me up and make me feel better. Once I found my purpose, my need for stuff almost completely diminished (rather ironically as I was then at the helm of a global magazine and got sent a lot of free stuff, most of which I gave away). Now that I am fulfilled and happy, I have less need for material things.

~~~~

Take the 'Am I emotionally intelligent?' quiz at
verywellmind.com and see how you rank.

TAKE A MOMENT TO WRITE DOWN HOW YOU FEEL DECLUTTERING COULD IMPACT YOUR LIFE. DO YOU WANT TO DECLUTTER YOUR HOME, YOUR MIND, YOUR LAPTOP? PERHAPS YOU'D LIKE TO FIND OBJECTS TO SELL, OR CREATE SPACE IN YOUR HOUSE FOR YOUR HOBBY. FOCUSING ON YOUR GOAL THROUGHOUT THE PROCESS WILL REMIND YOU THAT DECLUTTERING WILL BE WORTH THE EFFORT.

Write your monthly decluttering goal in the space below.

_____

_____

_____

_____

Lisa's Musing

For me, decluttering my mind, my space and my life enables me to think more clearly and make more space for what's really important to me. Trust me, it works if you work it.

"Every minute you spend looking through clutter, wondering where you put this or that, being unable to focus because you're not organised costs you: time you could have spent with family or friends, time you could have been productive around the house, time you could have been making money." – Jean Chatzky

**REARRANGE A SHELF: JUST ONE SHELF. START MOVING THINGS AROUND –
ADD A BOOK, MOVE A PLANT. CLEAR AWAY ANYTHING YOU DON'T NEED AND
THINK 'MINIMAL'. YOU DON'T NEED EVERYTHING ON DISPLAY, JUST A FEW
SELECT PIECES THAT MAKE YOU SMILE.**

Write down some of the reasons you have areas that are untidy or cluttered.
Do you have too much stuff? Is there a lack of storage?

_____

_____

_____

_____

_____

Lisa's musing

If you're like me, when you move in somewhere, I love the freshness of
a new place. Hence why we move a lot! For about the first six months
I'm nesting, moving things around, loving and soaking up my space.
Then the newness wanes a little. So this month we're going to try to
bring that excitement and that fresh new decluttered experience back
each and every day. Baby steps. Let's just start with one shelf.

Search 'bookshelves' in Pinterest and there is a trove
of inspiration and ideas for yours.

BUILDING FROM YESTERDAY, LET'S LOOK AT THOSE AREAS OF YOUR HOME YOU FEEL NEED TO BE DECLUTTERED.

Draw an outline of your house here and write down what needs to be done to make your home clean and ordered.

Lisa's Musing

One simple trick I do is to try to only have things on display that I really love. Everything else I put in cupboards or drawers. I also try to have a rule of 'one thing in, one thing out'.

For inspo for your home and garden, check out **tlcinteriors.com.au**.

OCTOBER 6

DO YOU NEED ALL THOSE SMARTPHONE NOTIFICATIONS? PARE IT BACK TO THE BARE ESSENTIALS LIKE MESSAGING AND TURN OFF THE REST. YOU MIGHT MISS A SALE BUT YOU WILL SAVE YOUR SANITY.

Answer these questions. Do you need notifications from:

Facebook	Yes No		TikTok	Yes No
Instagram	Yes No		Snapchat	Yes No
WhatsApp	Yes No		Twitter	Yes No
Shopify	Yes No		YouTube	Yes No
Email	Yes No		Other: _____	

Lisa's musing

I have no notifications turned on with the exception of texts and now Shopify (truth be told I'm addicted to the pings from sales). However, once the novelty wears off and we hit a consistent daily stride, I will endeavour to also turn those off. I couldn't care less about money for money's sake, but it's nice to see people enjoying our products, *and* the money coming in to pay for them all.

If you have a smart watch, you can check your apps on your wrist instead of on your phone, as well as pay for day-to-day items.

TECH CLEANSE #1: UNSUBSCRIBE FROM THOSE FILL-YOUR-INBOX-UP NEWSLETTERS. SET ASIDE 10 MINUTES TO GO THROUGH YOUR EMAIL AND UNSUBSCRIBE FROM ANYTHING THAT DOESN'T INTEREST OR SERVE YOU.

Write down five words that describe how you feel about your inbox. They can be positive or negative; it's however you feel about it.

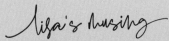

I have gotten into a bad habit and it's a terrible waste of time. Each morning I find myself just hitting delete, delete, delete about 20 times to all the unwanted newsletters I get. A much easier way than going in and unsubscribing from each individually is to use one of the tools mentioned here to just hit them all in one go.

Two tools that can help with this are Unlistr and unroll.me – these can do unscubscribe you in seconds.

OCTOBER 8

TECH CLEANSE #2: SPRING CLEAN YOUR PHONE CONTACTS. THIS IS A WAY TO REALISE HOW MANY PEOPLE YOU ACTUALLY WANT IN YOUR LIFE. ALSO, MAKE SURE YOU HAVE AN EMERGENCY CONTACT SAVED!

Write down the names of people you do need to include. Is it also time to update your emergency contact at work, your doctor, dentist, at your gym?

Lisa's Musing

Oh gosh, another note to self! Okay, I'm on it… as I'm writing this I realise I have a habit of 'I might need that someday' and it seems to be the same with people. So let's use a rule I use with clothes: if I haven't worn it for 12 months, re-homed it gets. Maybe if I haven't spoken to someone for five years (let's be generous) out they go!

Emergency+ is a free app developed by Australia's emergency services that uses the GPS of your phone to find out your exact location if you need help.

TIME TO TACKLE YOUR WARDROBE! WE ALL HAVE THOSE POCKETS OF CLOTHES WE DON'T FIT INTO. IT'S TIME TO GO THROUGH YOUR CLOTHES AND MAKE SURE YOU LOVE EACH ITEM. PUT YOUR FAVOURITE OUTFITS UP FRONT AND ANYTHING THAT MAKES YOU FEEL BAD ABOUT YOURSELF IN THE CHARITY BIN, GIVE IT AWAY, SELL ONLINE OR STORE IN VACUUM BAGS.

Write a list of people or places you could donate items to.

_____

_____

_____

_____

_____

Lisa's musing

Guilty. I seem to have gone up a (generous) size during COVID (anyone relate?), which is somewhat problematic. But it's a good excuse to a) ditch the things that I didn't really love or that don't bring me joy (hello, Marie Kondo), and b) get my butt moving and get back to pre-COVID weight!

~~~~~~~~

A starting point is this list of places you can donate to: **recyclingnearyou.com.au**.

GO THROUGH YOUR MAKE-UP DRAWER AND THROW OUT ANYTHING OLD, OUT OF DATE, CLUMPY, OR ANYTHING YOU'VE HAD FOR MORE THAN SIX MONTHS AND HAVEN'T USED. THEN, STREAMLINE YOUR MAKE-UP BAG AND GO SHOPPING FOR JUST WHAT YOU NEED. NO IMPULSE BUYS TODAY!

Write a list of what your minimal make-up bag should contain. Do you need to go shopping to refill it?

_____

_____

_____

_____

_____

Liga's musing

This chapter is probably my most challenging. I realise in writing this that I have absolutely no need for stuff, but the irony is that I feel bad getting rid of anything. The other irony is that I literally use one day cream, one night cream, one foundation, one bronzer, one lipgloss, one exfoliator, one body cream and very little of anything else. Off to charity, family and friends you go. I am super minimal in this area so why do I have all this stuff? Be gone! If I can do it, you can too.

"Time spent minimising possessions is never wasted." – Joshua Becker

ATTACK YOUR LINEN CUPBOARD – DO YOU HAVE TOWELS OR SHEETS WITH STAINS, THE WRONG SIZE FITTED SHEETS, AND BEACH TOWELS THAT YOU NEVER USE? NOW IS THE TIME TO GET ON TOP OF THAT. INVEST IN SOME COTTON, BAMBOO OR LINEN SHEETS AND FEEL THE DIFFERENCE.

Have you gone through your: sheets, pillowcases, rugs, towels, hand towels, tea towels, guest sheets/pillowcases. Do you need to replace any? Write your shopping list below if you need any new items.

_____

_____

_____

_____

_____

Lisa's Musing

Yes, gone. Easy peasy. It really is worth spoiling yourself a little on these items. Sleep is so important, and if you have one bed in your home, the most you need (truly) is two sets. So, be gone, linen and towels that we really don't need. I just gave a bunch to some uni student friends of mine and they were thrilled!

For beautiful sheets, see **ecolinen.com.au**, **thesheetsociety.com.au** and **linenrepublic.com.au**.

TECH CLEANSE #3: EVERYONE'S PHONES ARE AN 'APP CEMETERY'. TAKE 20 MINUTES TODAY TO GO THROUGH THE APPS ON YOUR PHONE AND ARRANGE THEM IN ORDER OF USE, DELETE ANY YOU DON'T USE AND DOWNLOAD ANY THAT YOU REALLY NEED.

App checklist:

- Clear unwanted apps

- Download any you need

- Organise into groups

- Put similar themes in folders

- Clean up your home screen

lisa's musing

Okay, fess up. I just deleted 27 apps… whoops! There were things on my phone I really have never ever used. I feel lighter already. I also moved all my faves to my home screen.

If you constantly forget your passwords, try LastPass Password Manager.

OCTOBER 13

THAT WALLET OF YOURS GETS A GOOD WORKOUT. IT'S TIME TO SORT THROUGH ALL THE CARDS, RECEIPTS, PHOTOS AND PAPERS THAT WE CRAM IN THERE. MAKE IT SUPER SLEEK AND HAVE A SECOND WALLET FOR ANY OLD CARDS YOU NEED TO KEEP BUT NEVER USE.

List what cards you need in your wallet on a day-to-day basis.
Anything else, file away or throw away.

_____

_____

_____

_____

_____

_____

Lisa's musing

I use my phone to pay for everything now, so I don't even carry a wallet. I keep my driving licence in the car and I've only been caught out a couple of times with needing cash.

〜〜〜

"Organisation isn't about perfection; it's about efficiency, reducing stress and clutter, saving time and money and improving your overall quality of life." – Christina Scalise

TECH CLEANSE #4: GO THROUGH YOUR SOCIAL MEDIA ACCOUNTS TODAY.

Answer these questions:

Which social media accounts do you need?

Which should be public and which should be private?

Do you need to start any new accounts on different platforms?

Who should you unfollow... is there anyone who impacts you negatively?

Lisa's Musing

Time consuming, sure, but how much time do you spend on your phone already mindlessly scrolling? Swap out a bit of that time today to clean some unnecessary clutter instead.

scrubber.social can search your social media account for embarrassing photos or captions that might stop you getting a job.

DO YOU HAVE A STACK OF BOOKS ON YOUR NIGHTSTAND, OR OVERFLOWING BOOKSHELVES? IT'S TIME TO TACKLE THEM! TAKE THEM ALL DOWN AND PUT THEM ALL IN ONE PLACE (MARIE KONDO-STYLE) AND MAKE THREE PILES. ONE TO DONATE, ONE TO KEEP AND ONE TO READ NEXT. PLACE THE READ NEXT PILE ALL TOGETHER ON ONE SHELF OR NEXT TO YOUR BED, SO THAT YOU'RE NOT TEMPTED TO BUY ANY NEW BOOKS UNTIL THAT PILE HAS GONE.

Write a list of all the books you don't own but want to read. Keep building on this list and return to it, once you have space in your pile to buy more!

_____

_____

_____

_____

Lisa's Musing

Books are my weakness (those and hot chips, slightly different outcomes!). I buy so many books. I love them. The crazy thing is I rarely read one cover to cover. With so much else going on in the world (and spending so much time writing them), I have become more of a page flicker. I will always buy and always support. But right now I am making a pile of books to donate and a fresh pile to read!

Where to donate books: secondhand bookstores, street libraries, charity stores, hospitals, retirement villages, hostels.

TECH CLEANSE #5: CLEAN UP YOUR DESKTOP ON YOUR COMPUTER. CREATE FOLDERS, FILE AND DELETE ITEMS YOU DON'T NEED. IF YOU'RE ONE OF THOSE PEOPLE WITH A DESKTOP THAT'S ALREADY CLEAN, LOOK AT YOUR FOLDERS AND DOCUMENTS. CAN THEY BE MORE ORGANISED?

Laptop checklist:

- Clean keyboard

- Back-up files

- Delete any old files that are not needed

- Clean desktop

- Empty trash/clear caches

Lisa's musing

Having owned businesses for over 19 years, I have a lot of 'stuff' on my laptop and on the cloud. I try to be super organised, but there is always more to be done.

Check out the free 'clean wallpaper' photos on **unsplash.com** to brighten up your desktop.

DECLUTTER THE PAPER TRAIL! SAY NO TO AS MANY PAPER BILLS AND LETTERS AS YOU CAN.

Paper trail to-do list:

- Log on to internet banking and request digital statements

- Advise your health insurance company you want digital notifications only

- Add a 'no junk mail' sticker to your letterbox

- Request digital versions of your tax and business statements

- Scan or take photos of any important documents so you always have them on hand (store them in a tidy folder on your desktop!)

Lisa's Musing

Much easier. Much more streamlined.
Much better for the environment.

~~~~~~~

Officeworks.com.au has a good range of storage
devices if you need extra room.

TECH CLEANSE #6: CURATE YOUR FEED: DON'T FORGET THAT YOU CAN CHOOSE WHAT YOU SEE ON SOCIAL MEDIA. SPEND 10 MINUTES CURATING WHO YOU FOLLOW AND WHAT YOU SEE.

Use the space below to list the feelings you associate with social media. Note: social media should make you feel good about yourself!

_____

_____

_____

_____

_____

Lisa's musing

When I joined Instagram (many moons ago), I think I just started following everyone. So it's taking quite a while to declutter. There is another way to do it. My friend Jamie recently hit 'unfollow' on everyone and has slowly been building up a carefully curated list of who he actually wants to follow. The 'Unfollow all' can take 30 seconds. The build up to that might take nine-and-a-half minutes.

"Minimising can be exhilarating. If you continue decluttering, you just might find a zest for life that you didn't know existed under all that stuff!" – Lisa J. Shultz

WHAT HABITS CAN YOU DECLUTTER? IS IT TIME TO GIVE UP SMOKING OR DRINKING? OR PERHAPS IT'S TIME TO START RUNNING OR MAKE BETTER USE OF YOUR GYM SUBSCRIPTION.

Take the time today to write down all the habits you have (good and bad) and see which ones you could streamline.

_____

_____

_____

_____

_____

_____

Lisa's Musing

On that note, a good thing to do is go through your latest credit card statement or other bills and go line by line, asking yourself which subscriptions you no longer really need. It is very liberating and it's amazing (and can be quite frightening) just how many can creep in there that you never actually use or need.

Watch Judson Brewer's TED talk,
A simple way to break a bad habit (**ted.com**).

TODAY, LET'S FOCUS ON STORAGE, THE DIGITAL KIND. TAKE A MOMENT TO MAKE SURE ALL OF YOUR IMPORTANT PHOTOS AND DOCUMENTS ARE STORED DIGITALLY USING ICLOUD, GOOGLE PHOTOS OR ANY OTHER SIMILAR SERVICES. HAVING A HARD DRIVE TO BACK-UP YOUR COMPUTER WILL ALSO HELP, AND IT ALLOWS YOU TO KEEP YOUR COMPUTER LESS CLUTTERED.

Make a list of all the important documents you need to keep, scan and file. We're talking birth certificates, tax returns, passports…

_____

_____

_____

_____

_____

_____

Lisa's musing

You do not want to lose these all-important memories.
So take some time to do this properly.

~~~~~~~

"Out of calmness comes clarity." – Trevor Carss

DECLUTTER YOUR SNACK ATTACK! IT'S HARD TO EAT HEALTHILY IF YOUR KITCHEN IS A MESS. TO HELP YOU, CREATE AN AREA IN YOUR CUPBOARD OR FRIDGE DEDICATED TO HEALTHY SNACKS: YOGHURT, LEFTOVERS, FRUIT, MUESLI BARS, ETC. HAVING THEM ON HAND WILL ENCOURAGE YOU TO REACH FOR A HEALTHY SNACK INSTEAD OF SOMETHING FULL OF SUGAR.

Write yourself a shopping list for snacks. Just snacks. What can you buy, make or freeze to give you healthy snacking options?

_____

_____

_____

_____

_____

Lisa's Musing

It's true: whenever I have sugar or chips or unhealthy snacks in my house, no matter how good I am being, there will come a time when I will reach for one. If they are not there, no reaching. Simple. Ditch the snacks you really don't want. Prepare healthy alternatives to keep you on track when you're feeling a little peckish.

For some healthy snack ideas, check out
kaylaitsines.com.au and **jaimieoliver.com**.

WE ALL HAVE THAT DRAWER OR OVERFLOWING FOLDER OF RECEIPTS. SCAN, PHOTOGRAPH OR USE AN APP TO DIGITISE YOUR RECEIPTS FOR THIS FINANCIAL YEAR AND SAVE SPACE. THIS IS A BIG JOB AND WE DON'T EXPECT YOU TO DO IT IN A FEW HOURS, SO MAKE A PLAN TO DO A LITTLE EVERY DAY UNTIL AT LEAST THIS YEAR IS SCANNED.

Make a list of all the financial years you need to scan and mark them off (month by month) until your past seven years are done.

Year: Scanned:

_____   _____

_____   _____

_____   _____

_____   _____

_____   _____

Lisa's Musing

This is a job I definitely outsource. Every time I get a receipt,
I take photo and send it to my trusty bookkeeper of almost 14 years.
Hire your weaknesses. Detail is definitely one of mine.

Some accounting apps to help with this are:
QuickBooks Online, FreshBooks, Xero, Hiveage.

LET'S KEEP THE MOMENTUM GOING BY CREATING A PERMANENT 'DONATE' BOX IN YOUR GARAGE OR LAUNDRY. AS YOU GO THROUGH THE DAY TODAY, MAKE A DECISION ABOUT THE THINGS YOU SEE, AND IF YOU DON'T USE THEM OR WON'T NEED THEM, THROW THEM IN YOUR DONATE BOX.

Make a list of where in your house you can look to find items to donate:

_____

_____

_____

_____

_____

_____

Lisa's musing

We have a donate box in our garage, and we try to throw a few things in there every day. I like the 'one in, one out' rule: if I bring something into the house, I take something out. There is a certain amount of satisfaction that comes from driving a full box to Vinnies.

If you're not sure of who to give your donations to, try **givit.org.au** who can help match your donation to a charity that needs it.

OCTOBER 24

WE'RE TACKLING OUR MEDICINE CUPBOARD TODAY. GO THROUGH YOUR MEDICINE, SUPPLEMENTS AND VITAMINS, THROWING OUT ANY THAT ARE PAST THEIR USE-BY DATE, OR ANY YOU JUST DON'T NEED. WITH YOUR VITAMINS, IF YOU DECIDE TO KEEP THEM, PUT THEM SOMEWHERE YOU'LL SEE THEM EVERY DAY SO YOU REMEMBER TO TAKE THEM.

Make a health plan and write down which vitamins and supplements you commit to taking every day.

Lisa's Musing

Gosh, we are powering! We're 24 days in and we are getting super tidy and decluttered. What a journey. If you're like me, this month is not easy. I have friction at every turn, but wow, what a difference it is making.

Search 'pill box' on Etsy for some really gorgeous supplement containers to help you remember to take them.

ROUTINES! WE LOVE ROUTINES, BUT DAYS CAN FILL UP PRETTY QUICKLY WHEN YOU'RE BUSY. LET'S DECLUTTER YOURS.

Write down below every personal commitment you have in a normal week. These can be anything from making dinner to volunteering commitments. Go through that list and see what you can cross off, what you feel obliged to do (but don't really need to) and what you can streamline.

_____

_____

_____

_____

_____

_____

_____

Lisa's musing

This is the declutter our diary part of the month. Now, you should be pretty well practised at this after the Power of Saying No month earlier this year! So, hopefully today's task is pretty smooth sailing.

"Minimalism is the constant art of editing your life." – Danny Dover

DO A BRAIN DUMP TODAY BEFORE YOU GO TO SLEEP. IF YOUR BRAIN IS FULL OF INFORMATION BEFORE BED, IT WILL TAKE LONGER FOR YOU TO NOD OFF. DOING THIS EVERY NIGHT CAN HELP WITH CREATING YOUR SHORT-TERM AND LONG-TERM TO-DO LISTS AS WELL.

Set a timer for 10 minutes and use this page to write down everything (and we mean everything) that comes into your brain. Now that's out of your head, you can deal with the list tomorrow!

If you need more space, transfer this list to a journal or a spare sheet of paper.

Lisa's musing

If you're an overthinker at night with a super-active brain, an idea is to keep a blank notepad by the side of your bed. When an idea strikes, turn over and write it down. For me, it makes going to sleep so much easier. It's out. I won't forget it. The 'to-do list' has it.

Sip on a cup of No.3 Sleeping Beauty tea from **ediblebeautyaustralia.com** to help you sleep.

LET'S GET BACK TO THE NITTY-GRITTY OF EVERYDAY CLUTTER. ONE AREA THAT TENDS TO ALWAYS NEED A CLEAN IS OUR CUPBOARDS. HOW MANY MISMATCHED MUGS AND GLASSES HAVE YOU COLLECTED? HOW MANY ARE SOUVENIRS OR UNWANTED PRESENTS? HOW MANY TAKEAWAY COFFEE MUGS DO YOU NEED? TAKE TIME TODAY TO CLEAN OUT THIS SECTION OF YOUR KITCHEN AND FILL UP YOUR DONATION BOX.

When you walk into your kitchen, how do you feel?
How does that compare to how you want to feel?

_____

_____

_____

_____

_____

_____

Lisa's musing

One person's trash is another's treasure. Unless you're going for a vintage, non-matchy-matchy vibe, let's just strip it back here, people.

"Have nothing in your home that you do not know to be useful or believe to be beautiful." – William Morris

OCTOBER 28

TODAY IS A BIGGIE. MAKE A LIST OF ALL THE DEBT YOU HAVE, INCLUDING CREDIT CARDS, AFTERPAY PAYMENTS, MORTGAGES, AND ANY MONEY YOU OWE OTHER PEOPLE. CAN YOU COMBINE DEBTS, PAY OFF SMALLER DEBTS FIRST, OR REMORTGAGE – ARE THERE WAYS TO REDUCE THIS DEBT? FINANCIAL FREEDOM ISN'T JUST ABOUT HAVING MONEY IN THE BANK, IT'S ABOUT MAKING SURE YOU AREN'T HELD BACK BY ONGOING DEBT.

Spend some time thinking about your finances. Use the space below
to get really transparent about where you're at and your goals.

I know this is a big ask. If you feel overwhelmed, we wrote a journal
similar to this, which literally has every spreadsheet and practical piece of
information in there to support you to get super financially organised.

Jump on to **shop.collectivehub.com** and purchase the *Know Your
Numbers Journal* to help you get on track with your finances.

ONE OF THE EASIEST WAYS TO DECLUTTER YOUR HOME (AND YOUR LIFE IN GENERAL) IS TO DEAL WITH THINGS AND SITUATIONS AS THEY ARISE. SO TODAY, AS SOON AS YOU GET HOME, EMPTY YOUR BAG AND PUT AWAY ANYTHING YOU CAN, THROWING OUT PACKAGING OR RUBBISH. THEN REPACK YOUR BAG FOR TOMORROW.

What are five things you could do when you walk in the door
that could help your future self in some way?

1. _____

2. _____

3. _____

4. _____

5. _____

Lisa's Musing

How tempting is it to get home and flop on the couch? Or do just about anything, except put everything away? I have very much trained myself with a 'do it as it happens' kind of mentality. It just stops things from mounting up and becoming overwhelming.

~~~~~~~

If you need inspiration, check out **organisemyhouse.com** for tips.

WE ALL LOVE REUSABLE BAGS, BUT THE PROBLEM IS WE TEND TO HAVE HUNDREDS OF THEM! TODAY, GATHER UP ALL YOUR SINGLE-USE PLASTIC BAGS AND MAKE A SPECIAL TRIP TO COLES OR WOOLWORTHS TO DROP THEM OFF IN THE REDCYCLE BOXES. THEN GO THROUGH YOUR REUSABLE BAGS AND CHOOSE FIVE TO EIGHT TO KEEP, AND DONATE THE REST.

List five other environmentally friendly habits you could pick up. Share them with us at #collectivehub or post a pic in our Facebook group (Collective Hub Club), we'd love to see your ideas so we can do them too!

1. _____

2. _____

3. _____

4. _____

5. _____

Lisa's Musing

The old plastic bag conundrum. We all have this. It's been such a topsy-turvy few years, and often we don't know which way is up in the world of bags. So, choose wisely, and choose what works for you.

∼∼∼∼∼

Find a range of sustainable goodies for your home at **Banish.com.au**.

FINALLY, THIS MONTH, TAKE A MOMENT TO COMMIT TO YOUR DECLUTTER RULES. CHOOSE FIVE TO FOLLOW. THESE COULD BE, "I AGREE TO EMPTY MY BAG AS SOON AS I GET HOME," "I AGREE TO ONLY BUY WHAT I NEED," ETC. CHOOSE REALISTIC RULES THAT WILL BENEFIT YOU GOING FORWARD.

My five declutter rules.

1. _____

2. _____

3. _____

4. _____

5. _____

Lisa's Musing

Ah…breathe a big sigh of relief. You have done so well this month. It was a big one. And your house and mind should be feeling pretty fab by now. So, yes, just choose five that you want to stick with and voilà, a clutter-free life awaits you!

"In the never-ending battle between order and chaos, clutter sides with chaos every time. Anything that you possess that does not add to your life or your happiness eventually becomes a burden." – John Robbins

november

TREAT YOURSELF

If you're anything like me, you live your life on the go. Each minute is filled with work, family, social catch-ups and more work, and you are constantly attached to your phone or laptop. Sound familiar?

Then this month is for you. Let's spend some energy over the next four weeks giving back by treating yourself and learning the art of self-care, self-appreciation and self-love.

We're not just talking about a hot bath sometimes or treating yourself to takeaway dinners (though those definitely count). We're talking about a total overhaul of how you perceive self-care.

We'll be looking at how to fit it into your already busy life, what self-care means for you, and how treating yourself can actually help you feel calmer and more in control of the things that matter to you.

LET'S START THIS MONTH OF SELF-CARE WITH A BRAINSTORM! WRITE DOWN BELOW WHAT COMES TO MIND WHEN YOU THINK OF SELF-CARE. WHAT ACTIONS, ACTIVITIES AND MOMENTS DO YOU THINK OF?

Answer these questions: When do you totally relax? When do you have the biggest smile on your face? When do you sleep the deepest?

_____

_____

_____

_____

_____

Lisa's Musing

Just quietly, did anyone else get as excited as me when we moved from a chapter on decluttering to a chapter on treating ourselves? Oooohhh, yeah! But you may also be someone who isn't great at looking after yourself and prioritising your needs. So you may feel challenged with this chapter. And that's okay. But I want this to become a space that is really all about you. Who are you and what do you need to feel nurtured? And breathe.

"Sometimes I give myself a break. So I will retreat a moment from the fray, just to breathe." – Michelle Obama

FOLLOWING ON FROM YESTERDAY, LET'S EXPLORE WHY YOU MIGHT NOT BE ABLE TO FIT SELF-CARE INTO YOUR LIFE REGULARLY.

Write down five reasons why you find it hard. These could be time-related, money-related, lack of motivation, lack of ideas, feelings of guilt. Whatever you feel might be holding you back, it's time to deep dive.

1. _____

2. _____

3. _____

4. _____

5. _____

It could also be as simple as you've never really prioritised yourself and therefore you really don't know what self-care looks like for you. So this is your time. Feel deeply into it.

"Maybe go outside for a few and feel the sunshine, or do a gorgeous mask, maybe treat yourself to the shoe you've been wanting. We have so much to rush for, so many things to fix and problems to solve, with all of that happening I'm trying to remind myself of self-care every day." – Jonathan Van Ness

NOVEMBER 3

MAKING TIME FOR SELF-CARE CAN BE HARD, SO COMMIT TO PUTTING ASIDE TIME FOR YOUR SELF-CARE AS YOU WOULD ANY OTHER MEETING.

Write down the schedule you will commit to. It could be as specific as booking a massage every Wednesday lunchtime, or as general as 'me time'. Blocking out time and putting it in your calendar will help you to not cancel it, and it will be something you can look forward to.

Lisa's musing

Now, this is big. I know so many busy people who simply will not prioritise their own self-care. Yet when someone suddenly needs their time, they can always find a space. If you can do it for a meeting or for someone else, you can certainly do it for yourself. No more excuses!

"When I take the time to take care of myself, to go to the doctor, go to a spa, get a deep-tissue massage, get adjusted by chiropractor... I feel like I can face life with a renewed vigor and renewed passion" – Viola Davis

LET'S START OFF WITH SOMETHING FUN. FORGET YOUR USUAL BUN OR PONYTAIL AND INSTEAD SPEND SOME TIME ON YOUR HAIRDO. IF YOU ARE ABLE TO, BOOK A BLOW-DRY OR A HAIRCUT. TRUST ME, WALKING OUTSIDE WITH 'FRESH' HAIR CAN TURN YOUR DAY AROUND.

While you are at the hairdresser today, make a list of all the self-care activities you would love to create time for in your life.

_____

_____

_____

_____

_____

Lisa's Musing

Confession time: I am terrible at doing my own hair. I am a fairly ripe age now and it's one thing that has eluded me my entire life. Having said that, I feel 100 per cent better and more confident with great hair. So, I fairly regularly have a blow-dry. My hairdresser knows me well: say hi, then let me do my work. It's where I get a lot of writing done, multitasking is super important to me. And I don't feel guilty for the pampering time (or my inability to do my own 'do).

We love the caffeinated scalp scrubs and hair mask from **frankbody.com**.

REWATCH AN EPISODE OF YOUR FAVOURITE SHOW: YES, THAT ONE YOU'VE ALREADY SEEN 97 TIMES. MAKE YOURSELF SOME POPCORN OR A CUP OF TEA AND SETTLE IN. GUILT-FREE.

What are your favourite shows to rewatch? List five.

_____

_____

_____

_____

_____

_____

Lisa's Musing

Now I'm not one to go back and do the same thing twice too often – let alone 97 times. But sometimes for a complete zone out, there's nothing better than revisiting one of your faves. Somehow it feels like we're living part of a completely different world just for a brief moment. For me it's fun to escape, explore and play in this way. Without having to think too much.

Hello, *Sex and the City*, *Friends*, *Seinfeld* and *Younger*…

CHANGE THE SHEETS ON YOUR BED TODAY, THEN HAVE A SHOWER BEFORE YOU SLEEP. IT SOUNDS SIMPLE, BUT GETTING IN BETWEEN FRESH SHEETS IS PURE LUXURY. SET A REMINDER IN YOUR PHONE OR CALENDAR TO CHANGE YOUR SHEETS EVERY WEEK. IT'S EASY TO LOSE TRACK, SO SETTING A REMINDER WILL HELP THIS BECOME A HABIT.

What other before-bed activities could you do to create
a calming environment for sleeping?

Freshly washed and dried sheets… I guarantee you will have the best
night's sleep all week tonight. How easy was today? Yum.

*"It is so important to take time for yourself and
find clarity. The most important relationship is the
one you have with yourself."* – Diane von Furstenberg

FIND TIME TODAY TO VISIT A CAFE, ORDER A DRINK AND SAVOUR IT. TURN YOUR PHONE OFF AND JUST CONCENTRATE ON REALLY ENJOYING THE TIME TO YOURSELF.

Just before you leave, use this page to write down how you feel. Are you more calm? Did you use the time to relax, or did you end up thinking about your to-do list?

_____

_____

_____

_____

_____

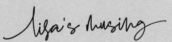

This is actually a great (and potentially quite challenging) exercise. It is simple, but I challenge you to sit at that cafe and, while you are drinking, resist the temptation to busy yourself. Don't pick up the menu, a paper, a book or anything. Sit there feeling confident that you don't have to look busy when in public and that you are not less than because you are sitting alone. Enjoy.

If you love cafe sounds, try **coffitivity.com** for background cafe noise while you work.

GET NUDE: WALK AROUND YOUR BEDROOM NAKED FOR A FEW MINUTES BEFORE GETTING DRESSED (YES, REALLY!). IT'S PROVEN TO IMPROVE SKIN HEALTH, BODY IMAGE AND EVEN SLEEP PATTERNS. THIS IS A1 SELF-CARE.

How does being naked make you feel? Explain why.
Go into detail on your feelings while being naked.

_____

_____

_____

_____

_____

_____

_____

_____

Lisa's musing

Well, I sleep nude every night. Always have. Always will.
Too much information? Ha!

"I only wear Chanel No. 5 to bed." – Marilyn Monroe

NOW TODAY'S ACTIVITY MIGHT NOT SEEM LIKE SELF-CARE, BUT THERE'S A REASON BEHIND IT (AND WE HAVE TALKED ABOUT THIS BEFORE)! AT THE END OF YOUR SHOWER TODAY, FINISH WITH A QUICK BURST OF COLD WATER. WHY? YOU'LL GET A BIG BURST OF ENERGY, AND STUDIES SHOW IT COULD ALSO RELEASE ENDORPHINS. IT'LL START THE DAY WITH A BANG!

How did you feel about your shower? Love it? Hate it?
Did it wake you up faster? Write about your experience below.

_____

_____

_____

_____

_____

Lisa's Musing

Aim for 40 seconds, if you can. Freezing cold. You'll feel great. I've gone one step further from time to time and done a fully immersive ice bath. In the summer of 2020/21 I did regular ice baths in an actual freezer in the Byron Bay hinterland. Check it out on my Instagram TV! Now that will take your breath away.

"A morning contrast shower works as a gym, sauna and spa in your bathroom." – Stan Jacobs

PUT ASIDE 30 MINUTES TODAY TO READ. YOU COULD DIVE INTO A NOVEL, LEARN WITH A SELF-HELP BOOK OR RELAX WITH A MAGAZINE. WHATEVER WORKS FOR YOU.

What is the book that has inspired you the most? What did you learn from it?

_____

_____

_____

_____

Lisa's Musing

I've spent quite a lot of time at the Osho Meditation retreat, and I have been fortunate enough to go through his extraordinary library. It is said that he read up to 10 books a day. We can train ourselves to read. It is a discipline like any other. It's trickier these days with so much content coming at us from so many channels and in such snackable bursts. It's also easy to switch on Netflix and zone out. But reading. One thing. For 30 minutes. Now that's discipline. A delicious, mindful discipline.

"Reading is essential for those who seek to rise above the ordinary."
– Jim Rohn

NOVEMBER 11

GIVE YOURSELF A BREAK AND ORDER IN YOUR DINNER TODAY. IF IT'S A LARGE PORTION, KEEP HALF FOR LUNCH OR DINNER TOMORROW. IN THE TIME YOU SAVE, PUT YOUR FEET UP AND RELAX.

How do you approach dinner time? Is it something you enjoy?
Do you love cooking? What are some ways you could enjoy it more?

_____

_____

_____

_____

_____

_____

Lisa's musing

See how things that might have been everyday normalities
before, suddenly become a little treat? Enjoy. Order whatever
you feel like. You deserve this.

Obvious ways to do this are UberEats and Menulog, but if you can
order directly at your local restaurant, it'll help them out a little more.

ENJOY A LONG 20-MINUTE STRETCHING SESSION THIS MORNING, AND EITHER LIGHT YOUR FAVOURITE CANDLE OR USE AN OIL DIFFUSER TO FILL THE AIR WITH RELAXING SMELLS.

Do a quick body scan before you start – mark up on this page where you hold tension and where you might need to focus on.

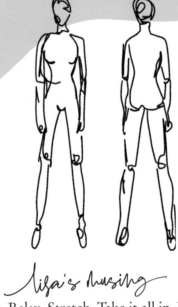

liga's musing

This is your time. Relax. Stretch. Take it all in. Nurture yourself and feel wonderful. Have a beautiful rest of the day!

Beautiful candles can be found at **dusk.com.au, lilyandbird.com.au, prettyfrank.com.au**.

LET'S LOOK AT ALL THE REASONS THAT MIGHT BE PREVENTING YOU SLEEPING BETTER. HOW MANY DO YOU HAVE CONTROL OVER? TONIGHT, GIVE YOURSELF A TREAT AND GO TO BED A LITTLE EARLIER. IF YOU'RE NOT TIRED, MEDITATE, READ A BOOK OR PRACTICE CALM BREATHING.

Use the space below to list some of the ways you could sleep better.

_____

_____

_____

_____

_____

_____

Lisa's Musing

It always shocks people when I say I sleep eight to 10 hours every night. I've tried to go through stints where I get up earlier and shorten my sleep cycle. But this seems to work for me and I am rarely tired. I have oodles of energy in abundance. Sleep is key! Try some magnesium before bed and switch off the tech at least 40 minutes beforehand.

Search white noise or 'baby lullaby' (yes, really!) on Spotify for some calming tunes.

SOMETIMES ALL YOU NEED IS A CHAT WITH SOMEONE YOU LOVE.

Write down the names of five friends, family members or mentors you want to speak to, and then the reason why. Call one today and spend 15 minutes treating yourself to an indulgent chat about everything and nothing.

1. _____

2. _____

3. _____

4. _____

5. _____

Lisa's Musing

I know, I know. It's sometimes easier just to send a quick text. Often there's no such thing as jumping on a 'quick call', but it's really important. I consciously choose the people I really want to have a good connection and catch up with. And then I purposefully remove all distractions so that I remain present for the call. Just allow some time and try to do at least a few of these a week.

Find new friends with Bumble BFF (**bumble.com/bff**) and meet new people in your area.

TODAY WE WANT YOU TO BECOME IMMERSED. "IN WHAT?" WE HEAR YOU ASK. ANYTHING THAT WILL HIJACK YOUR MIND FOR A LITTLE BIT. IT COULD BE CRAFT-RELATED, CREATING A VISION BOARD, PLAYING AN INSTRUMENT, ORGANISING A BOOKSHELF. IT'S YOUR CHOICE.

Write a list of five immersive activities you enjoy,
then revisit this page when you need to treat yourself!

1. _____

2. _____

3. _____

4. _____

5. _____

Lisa's Musing

I'm choosing puzzles today. I recently started doing them. I started with a 36-piece jigsaw with my four-year-old niece. Then jumped to a 64-piece one. I then got a little over zealous and bought a 1000-piece one. Turns out it just frustrated me (and the rest of the family). Rome wasn't built in a day. Baby steps. Try something. Do the simple, easy version. Then, if you like it, keep upping your game.

Learn a new skill with online classes for creatives at **domestika.org**.

IT'S A PLAN! SOMETIMES, JUST THE THOUGHT OF YOUR NEXT HOLIDAY IS ENOUGH TO PUT A BIG SMILE ON YOUR FACE. GRAB A CUPPA OR A COOL DRINK AND START PLANNING YOUR NEXT GETAWAY.

Use this page to decide the location, how you are getting there, what sort of place you would like to stay in and who is going with you.

_____

_____

_____

_____

_____

Lisa's musing

So, how was 2020? Not sure what year you're reading this, but remember the time we actually literally could not travel. I live in NSW and we were pretty lucky for most of the year, but what an odd concept that you could only travel within your state. Certainly that's never happened in our lifetime. But the silver lining? It did teach us to enjoy the wonders of our own backyard. Where will you go this year? Have fun with this!

~~~~~~~~~~~~~~~

Check out **@lostcontinent** on instagram for sustainable holiday accommodation.

TREAT YOURSELF WITH A LONG, RELAXING BATH TODAY.
CANDLES, BATH SALTS, MUSIC – THE WORKS!

Write a list here of all the things you need to have a perfect bath.
Make sure you aren't disturbed by leaving your phone outside the bathroom
on silent, and telling flatmates/partners/kids/pets not to bother you!

1. _____

2. _____

3. _____

4. _____

5. _____

Lisa's Musing

Is there anything more relaxing? I love candles, music, some great bath
soaks, dimmed lights, and I close my eyes, sink deep into the warmth
and weightlessness of the water. And straight away I am relaxed and
calm. It's a wonderful way to wash away the troubles of the day.

*"I have a bath every single day of my life. And if I can have
two or three – amazing. Nothing terrible is going to happen in the
bath, so I always find time for that. I'll take phone conversations
in the bath, anything."* – Emma Watson

SHORT AND SIMPLE: PREPARE OR ORDER YOUR FAVOURITE FOOD TODAY, AND SIT DOWN TO EAT AND ENJOY IT SLOWLY. TRY TO DO IT WITH NO DISTRACTIONS, NO PHONES OR TVS IN SIGHT.

Write down why you've chosen this meal - and how it makes you feel when you eat it. Remember to share a pic of it with us #collectivehub or post it in our Facebook group: Collective Hub Club.

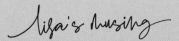

Oh, the choices! How delicious. Just a simple, super easy day for you today. Enjoy, and I can't wait to see what you choose.

For recipes ideas see Sydney-based nutritionist Amy Savage's website, **amysavagenutrition.com**.

UPDATE YOUR PHOTO AND BIO ON LINKEDIN. BY HAVING TO WRITE ABOUT WHO YOU ARE AND WHAT YOU HAVE ACHIEVED, YOU'LL BE GIVING YOURSELF A VIRTUAL PAT ON THE BACK.

Write down here the points you'd like to focus on, the kinds of words you want to describe yourself with, and info to delete from your profile.

_____

_____

_____

_____

_____

_____

Lisa's musing

Note to self: time I did mine! I remember when I first entered some awards years ago, it was great practice having to go back and remember and write down all my achievements. Try to do it as you go so that you don't have to go searching the corners of your mind later. From time to time you will need to do this, so might as well start today.

For help with this, check out the blog at **business.linkedin.com** – it has some helpful advice, straight from the horse's mouth.

NOVEMBER 20

GRAB YOURSELF A FACE MASK, A CALMING DRINK AND COMFY CLOTHES. THEN WHILE YOUR MASK IS DOING ITS MAGIC, WRITE DOWN FIVE THINGS THAT ALWAYS MAKE YOU LAUGH. ENJOY YOUR LITTLE ENDORPHIN HIT.

Share them with us #collectivehub or on our
Facebook group: Collective Hub Club.

1. _____

2. _____

3. _____

4. _____

5. _____

Lisa's Musing

If you're like me and don't drink, try making yourself a mocktail to enjoy while you do this exercise. It's so good to remember what makes us laugh and to focus on that. Laughter is a really important part of my life and I try to do it as much as possible!

For some great mocktail recipes, check out
nutritionstripped.com/your-guide-healthy-mocktails.

TODAY, LET'S GO TO THE SUPERMARKET. BUT DON'T BUY ANYTHING YOU ACTUALLY NEED. THIS IS AN INDULGENCE TRIP. TREAT YOURSELF WITH A PACKET OF CHOCOLATE BISCUITS, SOME BATH SOAK, AND YOUR FAVOURITE CHEESE. OR PERHAPS YOU'D LIKE TO TRY THREE THINGS YOU'VE NEVER TRIED BEFORE. EXPERIMENT, GO CRAZY.

What are three new meals or foods you'd love to try?

1. _____

_____

2. _____

_____

3. _____

_____

Lisa's musing

Oh, chocolate… As I write this, I haven't had sugar for some time. Now all I can think of is chocolate. So if you're also not eating sugar because it was something that resonated from a previous exercise, then try a food from a region you don't normally experiment with.

To mix it up a little visit your local grocer, an IGA supermarket, Harris Farm, your local Chinatown, and try something new!

GO FOR A DRIVE WITH THE WINDOWS OPEN AND YOUR FAVOURITE TUNES ON REPEAT. ENJOY THE FEELING OF FREEDOM WHILE SINGING AT THE TOP OF YOUR LUNGS. IF YOU DON'T HAVE A CAR, VISIT YOUR LOCAL PARK OR COASTLINE, FEEL THE WIND IN YOUR HAIR AND BLAST YOUR EARPODS!

What three songs do you love singing? How do they make you feel?

1. _____

   _____

2. _____

   _____

3. _____

   _____

Lisa's musing

There's nothing like a good road trip. I have a few mates with guitars and sometimes we get together for a super fun night of jamming. No talking. Just loads of singing and dancing.

Time Out's top six karaoke songs are: *Purple Rain* by Prince, *Like a Prayer* by Madonna, *Private Eyes* by Hall & Oates, *Shallow* by Lady Gaga and Bradley Cooper, *Let's Get It On* by Marvin Gaye, *I Want It That Way* by the Backstreet Boys.

PUT ON YOUR FAVOURITE FORMAL OUTFIT, COMPLETE WITH JEWELLERY, HANDBAG AND MAKE-UP, AND MEET A FRIEND FOR COFFEE OR INVITE A FRIEND OVER FOR AFTERNOON TEA. GET DRESSED TO THE NINES, LIKE OUR GRANDMOTHERS DID. SHARE A PHOTO WITH US #COLLECTIVEHUB OR ON OUR FACEBOOK GROUP: COLLECTIVE HUB CLUB!

Clothes can make or break your day – explain your three favourite pieces of clothing and how they make you feel.

1. _____

2. _____

3. _____

Lisa's Musing

I'm not a formal kinda gal, but my grandmother, Lady Fuller (my grandfather was knighted by the Queen), was the most impeccable dresser. She was always immaculate and wore heels till her last day. Her hair was always perfectly coiffed and her fashion sense was out of this world. There is something very beautiful, glamorous and special about that era. I often look to my good friend Kerrie Hess (**@kerriehessillustration**) and think she is always so beautifully presented with her style, grace and beautiful garments.

~~~~~~~~

Found some clothes you don't need? Donate them to this great cause: **dareformalwear.com.au.** They will be distributed to Year 12 students who can't afford formal dresses for their end-of-year celebrations.

NOVEMBER 24

WATCH THE SUNSET OR SUNRISE BY YOURSELF OR WITH A GOOD FRIEND. APART FROM TAKING A PHOTO TO SHARE WITH US, STAY OFF YOUR PHONE. JUST WATCH. RELAX. AND ENJOY.

Describe two of the best sunrises or sunsets you've ever seen. Who were you with? And why did you love them so much?

_____

_____

_____

_____

_____

_____

Lisa's Musing

Whenever I'm home, I try to walk down to North Bondi on the Grassy Knoll at least a few times a week and watch the sunset. It is just stunning and a certain calm washes over me.

The Sunrise Sunset Times app helps with knowing exactly when the sunrise and sunset will start and finish.

GO FOR A PICNIC! EITHER SOLO OR WITH FRIENDS – IT COULD JUST BE IN YOUR LOCAL PARK OR A NEARBY NATIONAL PARK. TAKE A RUG, FOOD AND DRINK, AND SOME MUSIC, AND ENJOY A SHORT RELAX ON THE GRASS.

Use the space below to plan your packing list
of everything you'll bring to the picnic.

_____

_____

_____

_____

_____

_____

_____

Lisa's Musing

One of my fave things to do. Firstly the art of putting
it together is super fun. But then just getting out in nature
and relaxing. Pure bliss for me.

Beautiful picnic rugs can be found at **wanderingfolk.com**.

IGNORE YOUR BOOK PILE AND RE-READ AN OLD FAVOURITE.

1. What book did you choose?

2. Where were you in life the first time you read this book?

3. Is it as good as you remember or has it (or you) changed?

Share a pic of your book with us #collectivehub or post in our
Facebook group (Collective Hub Club) so we can check it out too!

Lisa's Musing

I'd love to know what you think. It's a funny thing when you revisit
something years later. Does it still hold true? Have you changed?
And if you have a different response or reaction to it, why? Have you
grown? Have your values or beliefs or perceptions changed?

*"Let's be reasonable and add an eighth day to the week
that is devoted exclusively to reading."* – Lena Dunham

WE'RE BRINGING BACK A LITTLE MEDITATION FOR TODAY AS IT'S JUST SO GOOD FOR US. TREAT YOURSELF TO A 15-MINUTE MEDITATION BEFORE BED TONIGHT. LET YOUR MIND RELAX AND ENJOY THE SILENCE.

If you prefer, put on some calming music and use your meditation time to draw in the space below. Doodle anything that comes to mind. Share your drawing with us #collectivehub or post it in our Facebook group: Collective Hub Club. We'd love to see it! We'll post ours too.

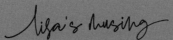

Ooh you've learned and practised so many kinds of meditation! As a refresher, go back to April and choose one of your favourites. Let me know which one you love the most.

"Meditation also has been a wonderful tool. I notice that when I don't take the time to do it, I am not as centred, patient or clear." – Gisele Bündchen

MOISTURISE YOUR ENTIRE BODY. NOT ONLY IS IT A TREAT FOR YOUR SKIN, IT'S ACTUALLY A VERY EFFECTIVE SELF-SOOTHING ACTIVITY.

Use this space to write down all the thoughts that come
into your head as you do this mindful activity.

_____

_____

_____

_____

_____

_____

Lisa's Musing

I'm super-duper conscious these days of what I put on my body.
Mostly I choose to use vegan moisturisers with healthy ingredients.
One of my current faves is Bangn Body. I'm also a long-time lover
of most things The Body Shop produces.

Some clean beauty favourites are:
Maaemo, Mukti and Black Chicken Remedies.

GET TO KNOW YOURSELF INTIMATELY. OKAY, WE'RE ALL ADULTS HERE. NO NEED TO BE EMBARRASSED. TODAY HAVE A LITTLE ALONE TIME IN BED!

What makes you feel sexy and attractive? How can you encourage that?

Lisa's musing

I'll just leave this one there.

~~~~~~~~~

For short and sexy audio stories to get you in the mood (their words, not ours), try **dipseastories.com**.

REVISIT YOUR SELF-CARE ROUTINE FROM DAY 3 OF THIS MONTH AND SEE IF YOU WANT TO UPDATE IT, ADD ACTIVITIES IN OR EXPAND ON WHAT YOU HAVE. COMMIT TO THIS NEW SCHEDULE FOR THE NEXT FEW MONTHS.

Rewrite and refine your routine below:

_____

_____

_____

_____

_____

_____

_____

Lisa's musing

Wow, another month. So damn proud of you. How are you feeling?
Give yourself a big pat on the back. Really. It's pretty extraordinary.
Alrighty then, let's jump into December. I'm so looking forward
to the next part of the journey with you.

Listen to The Self-Care Project by Jayne Hardy
on Audible for inspiration.

What have you enjoyed the most about this month? What have you learned?

_____

_____

_____

_____

_____

_____

_____

_____

_____

_____

_____

_____

_____

_____

_____

_____

december

GIVE THANKS

Congratulations! You've almost made it to the end of the year!

And while it's been an amazing ride so far, focusing on everything from creativity to productivity, this month we're asking you to take a step back and practise gratitude, all month long.

Highlighting all the great things in your life is especially important as one year ends and another begins, full of promise and opportunities.

However, being grateful isn't just something your grandmother told you to do; it comes with a swag of pretty serious health benefits, too. Studies show that practising gratitude can improve our relationships, reduce feelings of stress, increase motivation and boost our mood.

So, what are you waiting for? Let's start appreciating everything and everyone we have in our life right now.

DECEMBER 1

THIS MONTH WE ARE GOING TO FOCUS ON ALL THE GREAT PEOPLE AND THINGS IN YOUR LIFE. TODAY, LIST EIGHT MOMENTS YOU'RE GRATEFUL YOU HAVE EXPERIENCED IN YOUR LIFE SO FAR.

1. _____

2. _____

3. _____

4. _____

5. _____

6. _____

7. _____

8. _____

Lisa's Musing

In 2020 my team and I put out a Gratitude Journal, because it's something I've been practising for years. And something that has made an extraordinary difference in my life. I am 'grateful' you have bought this book and that you are here with me.

"Appreciation is a wonderful thing. It makes what is excellent in others belong to us as well." – Voltaire

DECEMBER 2

TAKE A MOMENT TO LIST THE REASONS YOU ARE GRATEFUL TO BE LIVING RIGHT NOW IN THIS DECADE (THINK: MODERN MEDICINE, AIR TRAVEL, SPACE TRAVEL, ETC). WE SPEND A LOT OF TIME READING THE NEWS AND FOCUSING ON WORLD EVENTS, WHICH CAN BE ALL DOOM AND GLOOM, SO TODAY LET'S CONSIDER HOW LUCKY WE ARE.

_____

_____

_____

_____

_____

_____

_____

There are so many reasons to be grateful. Truly. And this month I want to remind you about mindset flipping. We can't control what comes at us every day, but we can control how we respond to it.

"When you arise in the morning give thanks for the food and for the joy of living. If you see no reason for giving thanks, the fault lies only in yourself" – Tecumseh

DECEMBER 3

CREATE A GRATITUDE JAR NEAR YOUR BED WITH A PEN AND PAPER CLOSE BY. EVERY MORNING AND EVENING THIS MONTH, WRITE ONE THING YOU ARE GRATEFUL FOR IN YOUR LIFE RIGHT NOW. WE WILL REVISIT THIS JAR AT THE END OF THE MONTH.

To get you in the mood, write down five things you are grateful for today.

_____

_____

_____

_____

_____

_____

_____

I've done this sporadically over the years. You can choose to do it in a journal or in a jar. A jar is fun! When you're feeling a little down, you can reach in and remember something wonderful about life.

Use **dayoneapp.com** to record all the things you are grateful for, either with images or words.

WRITE YOURSELF A LETTER TODAY AND THANK YOURSELF FOR ALL THE GREAT QUALITIES YOU HAVE. INCLUDE ALL THE THINGS YOU LOVE ABOUT YOURSELF. WRITE IT AS IF YOU ARE WRITING TO YOUR FRIEND.

Dear me,

_____

_____

_____

_____

_____

_____

From me xx

Lisa's Musing

You can go one step further: write it out on nice paper, seal it up and address it to yourself. Pop a stamp on it and ask a friend to mail it to you unexpectedly at a time they feel is right.

Download the app After Time, add your letter, and it will send it back to you on a random date.

COMPLIMENT SOMEONE, BUT NOT ABOUT THEIR APPEARANCE. TELL THEM WHY YOU'RE GRATEFUL TO HAVE THEM IN YOUR LIFE, WHY THEY MAKE YOU SMILE, HOW THEY INSPIRE YOU, ETC.

Write down a list of people you can contact this week for a catch-up:

_____

_____

_____

_____

_____

_____

_____

_____

Lisa's musing

So important and refreshing. How often do we get caught up in appearances? How much more depth is there to someone? It not only gives them a boost, but it gets us thinking on a deeper level.

For 100 compliment ideas, search "compliments" on **happier.com**.

SAY THEIR NAME: ASK YOUR BARISTA/FLORIST/WAITER THEIR NAME, AND THANK THEM FOR THEIR CONTRIBUTION TO YOUR DAY.

Write down their names here so you don't forget!

_____

_____

_____

_____

_____

_____

Lisa's Musing

When you remember someone's name and you use it, boy, what a difference it makes! Think about when someone remembers and uses your name. Or, even better, when they use an abbreviation of it like 'Lis' instead of 'Lisa'. I instantly feel we're best friends. Okay, I get that it might really irk some people. Horses for courses!

Have trouble remembering names? Search "remember people's names" on **ideas.ted.com** for simple techniques.

WRITE A POSITIVE REVIEW FOR A SMALL BUSINESS. TAKE THE TIME TO LEAVE A REVIEW FOR A BUSINESS YOU RECENTLY HAD A POSITIVE INTERACTION WITH. IT CAN GO A LONG WAY FOR A SMALL OPERATION.

Write down three businesses you could review over the coming week. Explain what you like about them.

_____

_____

_____

_____

_____

_____

Every time you do this, a small business owner actually does do a little happy dance. For real.

Ways to do this: Google reviews, Facebook reviews, comment on a post, send an email, check what third-party websites they use (menulog, Etsy, Houzz etc).

GIVE YOUR FAVOURITE BOOK AWAY: BE GRATEFUL FOR A BOOK YOU ENJOYED BY GIVING IT TO SOMEONE ELSE SO THEY CAN DO THE SAME.

What book did you give away, who to, and why did you like it so much?

_____

_____

_____

_____

_____

_____

With so much content and so many books out there, how wonderful is it when you've enjoyed one so much you pass it on or buy a copy for a friend? I am a sucker for a great gifted book. And, to be honest, I love gifting my own ones whenever the opportunity arises.

"The reading of all good books is like conversation with the finest people of the past centuries." – Descartes

INVEST YOUR SUPPORT: FIND A CROWDFUNDING SITE, PICK A PROJECT THAT TAKES YOUR FANCY, AND INVEST IN THEIR (AND YOUR) FUTURE.

What project will you support and why do you like it?

How much can you commit to investing?

How do you feel about investing in someone else's dream?

Do you feel aligned with their vision? Explain why.

Lisa's Musing

It just feels so great to do this. You help someone with their dream and you own a little piece of something. It's such a win-win situation.

〜〜〜〜

Check out Kickstarter, GoFundMe, Indiegogo, Patreon, RocketHub.

VOLUNTEER: WHETHER YOU HELP SOMEONE TODAY OR A CHARITY IN THE FUTURE, ALTRUISM IS PROVEN TO MAKE YOU HEALTHIER AND LIVE LONGER!

Write down who you might be interested in volunteering for or donating to:

Lisa's Musing

Find a charity close to your heart and then find out what they need help with. One of my chosen charities is **foodbank.org.au**. I'll often grab a bunch of mates and go for a day of hamper packing. Last year we got our community to write 1,500 Christmas cards to pop in with the Christmas hampers. It was such a joy.

Try contacting these sites to help you find where to volunteer: **govolunteer.com.au**, **volunteer.com.au** and **volunteering.com.au**.

DECEMBER 11

GRATITUDE JOURNALLING DOESN'T HAVE TO BE A LONG-WINDED EXERCISE. AT THE END OF THE DAY, JUST PICK THREE THINGS YOU WERE GRATEFUL FOR. IT MIGHT BE AS SIMPLE AS THE WEATHER, A KIND WORD, A MOMENT OF QUIET OR A CALL FROM A FRIEND.

List your three gratitudes below:

_____

_____

_____

_____

_____

_____

_____

Lisa's Musing

This is an incredibly simple exercise and one I've been practising for many years. It's tricky to be angry when you have a constant stream of gratitude. Try to make it a daily practice.

Check out **collectivehub.com** or any good bookstore for our very own gratitude journal *Daily Gratitudes*.

DECEMBER 12

**CHOOSE ANYONE IN YOUR CONTACTS THAT YOU WANT TO GIVE SOME
LOVE TO AND SEND THEM A COMPLIMENT VIA TEXT MESSAGE.
A LOVELY LITTLE THOUGHT CAN MAKE SOMEONE'S DAY.**

Write down some more friends or family members you haven't
spoken to in a while, and text them to say hello!

_____

_____

_____

_____

_____

_____

Sometimes it may feel a little like going out on a limb. You may feel
a bit awkward if you haven't called them in ages, but this is exactly
the type of person I want you to call today. Take five minutes to
meditate before you do it and really feel into who might need some
of your energy today. Enjoy the feeling of connection!

*"The heart that gives thanks is a happy one, for we cannot feel
thankful and unhappy at the same time."* – Douglas Wood

FRIENDS MAKE THE WORLD GO AROUND. CHOOSE THREE FRIENDS, AND WRITE DOWN REASONS YOU'RE GRATEFUL THEY ARE IN YOUR LIFE.

List your friends and your reasons below:

Friend 1:   Reason:

_____   _____

_____   _____

Friend 2:   Reason:

_____   _____

_____   _____

Friend 3:   Reason:

_____   _____

_____   _____

Lisa's Musing

We often get so busy we can forget who our wonderful friends are or why we enjoy them so much. It's a lovely thing to do to write these things down. From time to time I also have a bunch of friends over for dinner and go around the table acknowledging something we are all grateful for about each other.

"It's a funny thing about life, once you begin to take note of the things you are grateful for, you begin to lose sight of the things that you lack." – Germany Kent

LET'S WORK ON A GRATEFUL MANTRA FOR THE TIMES WHEN YOU ARE FEELING LOW. WRITE DOWN 10 (YES, 10!) THINGS YOU ARE GRATEFUL FOR.

1. _____   6. _____

2. _____   7. _____

3. _____   8. _____

4. _____   9. _____

5. _____   10. _____

Lisa's Musing

Once you start, there are so many things you could choose from. Often they are super simple. As I write this right now, in this moment, here are some of mine: I am grateful for Benny dog snoring lovingly by my side. I am grateful for the rain on the plants and the smell of the fresh leaves. I am grateful to have so much joy in writing this book. I am grateful for the kick-arse training session I did this morning. I am grateful for the cuddles my partner gave me before he left the house this morning. I am grateful for our beautiful community, who connect with me and are courageous enough to share their journey.

Search 'happiness mantra' from Meditative Mind on YouTube for calming sounds and uplifting music.

DECEMBER 15

GRATITUDE PHOTO CHALLENGE. THROUGHOUT TODAY, PHOTOGRAPH ANYTHING THAT MAKES YOU SMILE. PERHAPS IT'S YOUR PUPPY, YOUR MORNING BREW, THE WAY THE LIGHT HITS THE TREES. BE CREATIVE AND DON'T HOLD BACK. SHARE THE PICS WITH US ON SOCIAL MEDIA.

Describe below your five favourite photos and why they made you smile.

1. _____

2. _____

3. _____

4. _____

5. _____

This is, in a way, one of the nice upsides of social media. It gives us an outlet to capture things and share them. Sometimes it's nice to not photograph them through the lens of 'will this look good on social media?' but genuinely because it is something that brings you joy and that you are grateful for. The more authentic you are, the more (the right) people will fall in love with you.

"Gratitude turns what we have into enough, and more. It turns denial into acceptance, chaos into order, confusion into clarity... it makes sense of our past, brings peace for today, and creates a vision for tomorrow." – Melody Beattie

TODAY, CREATE A MEMORY BOX. THIS IS A SMALL CONTAINER WITH ITEMS THAT SPARK WONDERFUL MEMORIES. THE IDEA IS TO HAVE A PLACE YOU CAN ACCESS TO REMEMBER THE AMAZING EXPERIENCES YOU HAVE SHARED AND PEOPLE YOU HAVE MET. ADD TICKET STUBS, PHOTOS, SHELLS, ANYTHING THAT IS CONNECTED TO A MEMORY YOU LOVE.

Write down a sentence about a few of the memories in your memory box. Why did that memory become so important?

_____

_____

_____

_____

_____

Lisa's Musing

I have many memory boxes from over the years. Every now and then I open them and floods of happy memories come back through the mustiness of old pieces of paper and trinkets. Sometimes I get sad (and that's okay) as I remember the passing of time, but that is also something to be grateful for and a reminder to cherish every moment.

Create an online memory box and share it with friends and family at **memories.com.au**.

CHECK IN WITH YOUR GRATITUDE JAR TODAY. HAVE YOU BEEN KEEPING UP WITH IT? ADD THREE THINGS ABOUT TODAY THAT YOU ARE GRATEFUL FOR.

Snap a pic of your jar and share it with us #collectivehub
or post in our Facebook group: Collective Hub Club.

1. _____
   _____

2. _____
   _____

3. _____
   _____

Pull a couple out from your jar to remind yourself what
amazing things the last 16 days have brought to your life.

~~~~~~~~~

*"In ordinary life, we hardly realise that we receive
a great deal more than we give, and that it is only with
gratitude that life becomes rich."* – Dietrich Bonhoeffer

LET'S THINK BACK TO YOUR CHILDHOOD. THINK ABOUT ALL THE EXPERIENCES YOU HAD, FRIENDS YOU LOVED AND SCHOOL DAYS YOU LAUGHED THROUGH.

Write down three childhood memories you are grateful for.

1. _____
   _____

2. _____
   _____

3. _____
   _____

Lisa's Musing

Three of my fave memories are galloping on my horse, jumping random logs, every day after school. Often with friends. Summer holidays on the beach frolicking and swimming all day. Listening to great music and making up dance moves with my girlfriends.

Want to contact your childhood friends? The Touchnote app allows you to send postcards and cards to anyone in the world.

GIVE SOMEONE FLOWERS TODAY. IT DOESN'T HAVE TO BE A BIG, EXPENSIVE BOUQUET – A SMALL HAND-PICKED ONE FROM YOUR GARDEN, OR EVEN A SMALL POTTED FLOWER WILL DO. MAKE SOMEONE SMILE.

When was the last time you received flowers?
Who were they from and how did they make you feel?

_____

_____

_____

_____

_____

_____

Lisa's musing

Any time someone wants to give me a gift, my fave most treasured present is either hand-picked flowers from your garden or an actual live growing plant. It seems I can never have too many of those.

Send flowers everywhere in Australia with **floraly.com.au** and they will buy a meal for someone at OzHarvest.

TIME FOR SELF-REFLECTION ON WHAT YOU TAKE FOR GRANTED.

Using this page, answer these questions: What are some of the things, people, places you take for granted? What are you guilty of ignoring?

_____

_____

_____

_____

_____

_____

There are a few people I've been neglecting who are certainly worthy
of much more of my love, time and appreciation. Also work out what
the love languages of those closest to you are. We all have different
ways of connecting. Find theirs and lay it on thick.

*"Wear gratitude like a cloak, and it
will feed every corner of your life."* – Rumi

SPEND THE DAY BEING AN OPTIMIST. THIS WILL FLEX YOUR GRATITUDE MUSCLES. MISSED THE BUS? WHAT A GREAT CHANCE TO WALK! RAINING? TIME TO PRETEND TO BE A LITTLE KID, JUMPING IN PUDDLES.

Use the space below to record three moments from today where you mindfully turned a negative situation into a positive experience.

1. _____

   _____

2. _____

   _____

3. _____

   _____

Lisa's Musing

Today is ALL about a mindset flip. WHATEVER happens, whatever comes at you, flip it. What's the upshot? This is an incredible and powerful practice and one I have honed over time.

Try the Happify app for exercises that train your brain to be optimistic. Visit **happify.com** to learn more.

DECEMBER 22

YOUR BODY IS AN AMAZING MACHINE, BUT IT RARELY GETS THE RECOGNITION IT DESERVES! TODAY, THINK ABOUT WHAT YOU LOVE ABOUT YOUR BODY, WHAT IT GIVES YOU EVERY DAY AND HOW IT SERVES YOU.

Write down five things you love about your body, your face and your brain.

1. _____

2. _____

3. _____

4. _____

5. _____

Lisa's Musing

Yes, let's be grateful. If you really stop and think about it, how absolutely and utterly mind blowingly incredible is it that this one vessel carries us around all day, every day. I know I've put mine through some pummellings over the years and it still serves me beautifully. I am so grateful for it.

Settle in and watch the popular documentary
The Amazing Human Body on Amazon Prime.

THINK OF ALL THE REASONS IT'S SO GREAT TO BE THE AGE YOU ARE. WHAT DO YOU LOVE ABOUT YOURSELF NOW? THINK ABOUT WHAT YOU'VE LEARNED IN LIFE SO FAR AND HOW THESE LESSONS HAVE SHAPED WHO YOU ARE TODAY.

Use the space below to list the top three reasons you love who you are.

1. _____

   _____

2. _____

   _____

3. _____

   _____

Lisa's Musing

Wisdom. Lessons. Experience. All these things come with age. Being young, being older – each of these things come with wonderful, joyful benefits. For me, age is attitude. In terms of numbers, I am ageless. A good question I often reflect on is: if I didn't know how old I was in years, how old would I be? Mind blown.

"Do not spoil what you have by desiring what you have not; remember that what you now have was once among the things you only hoped for." – Epicurus

LIST THREE THINGS YOU ARE LOOKING FORWARD TO IN THE FUTURE. WHY ARE YOU EXCITED BY THEM?

Describe your future fortunes!

1. _____

_____

2. _____

_____

3. _____

_____

Liza's Musing

So many wonders in the present – but having something to look forward to gives us a sense of purpose, excitement and drive. I'm looking forward to new adventures, getting fitter, stronger, healthier. Spending days with my beautiful partner and having kids together (God willing). Growing my business and community, and helping as many people as we can. So many things to look forward to.

Get a glimpse into the future with **futuretimeline.net**, set up by London-based writer and futurist William James Fox.

DECEMBER 25

TAKE A MOMENT TODAY, IN AMONG THE HUSTLE AND BUSTLE, TO THINK ABOUT ALL YOUR CHRISTMASES OR FAVOURITE HOLIDAYS. TODAY CAN BE SUCH A JOYOUS TIME FOR SOME, AND REALLY CHALLENGING FOR OTHERS. LET'S FOCUS ON THE BEST OF THE GOOD TIMES!

Write down your fave Christmas or holiday traditions
that you celebrate this time of the year:

_____

_____

_____

Lisa's musing

I've always had a fanciful fairy-tale notion of Christmas, but with a broken family it has rarely turned out the way I wanted, and my expectations have been dashed more often than not. So I decided to take back my Christmas power and do it my way. I play Christmas carols at full bore for a month before. I put up a tree and decorate it. I send cards and gifts and invite friends over. On Christmas Eve I write my visions for the next year. And on Christmas Day I make sure I spend a lot of time in nature. I do everything I can to make it the best it can be for me and those I love around me.

Create an online collage of your best holiday
snaps at **befunky.com/create/collage**.

ENGAGE IN A RANDOM ACT OF KINDNESS TODAY. PAY FOR SOMEONE'S COFFEE OR PARKING, OPEN A DOOR FOR SOMEONE, LEAVE A TIP FOR A WAITER. LEAVE A GIFT AT YOUR NEIGHBOUR'S DOOR. SHARE THE LOVE.

What did you do?

How did it make you feel afterward?

Lisa's Musing

Do it, and do it without expectation or recognition. Do it and then leave the scene never knowing the outcome. That's harder to do because it is less about your ego and more genuinely about an act of kindness. Okay, it's also pretty nice (and human nature) to see the smile or joy it brings to someone else.

"Gratitude is not only the greatest of virtues, but the parent of all others." – Marcus Tullius Cicero

BE THANKFUL FOR THE MISTAKES YOU'VE MADE AS THEY MAKE YOU THE PERSON YOU ARE. TODAY, THINK ABOUT SOME MISTAKES THAT HAVE SHAPED WHO YOU ARE TODAY.

List some mistakes you've made that have taught you a valuable lesson.

_____

_____

_____

_____

_____

_____

Lisa's Musing

Ha! Three… I make mistakes all day, every day. And I learn from them. Take responsibility, make amends if that is needed, and try to move on as quickly as possible. If I make the same mistake a second time, well then I'm not quite so kind to myself. We all make mistakes. Make them your friend.

Hear stories of mistakes and successes from some of Australia's most influential businesswomen at **shinebusinesswomen.com**.

HAND WRITE FIVE 'THANK YOU' CARDS TO FAMILY MEMBERS YOU APPRECIATE. YOU COULD THANK THEM FOR BEING A GREAT SUPPORT, FOR A GIFT THEY GAVE YOU, THE KINDNESS OF THEIR SOUL, THE WAY THEY MAKE YOU FEEL, OR JUST A QUICK THANK YOU FOR SIMPLY BEING THEM. IT'S TIME TO APPRECIATE THEM! DON'T FORGET 'FAMILY' CAN BE ANY LOVED ONE.

List the family members you'll write cards to and write a few words as to why you love them/are grateful for them in your life:

1. _____

2. _____

3. _____

4. _____

5. _____

Lisa's musing

How did that feel? This is one of my favorite acts. It brings me joy… the joy of writing. The joy of acknowledging another human. The joy of imagining them opening it. There is nothing to lose on this one.

Beautiful thank-you cards can be found at Typo, **hardtofind.com.au,** and Kikki-K.

DECEMBER 29

BEFORE YOU GET OUT OF BED, START THE DAY WITH A CONFIDENCE HIT BY REREADING THE LETTER YOU WROTE YOURSELF AT THE BEGINNING OF THE MONTH. DO YOU STILL BELIEVE EVERYTHING YOU WROTE?

Use the space below to list the compliments that stand out from your letter.

_____

_____

_____

_____

_____

_____

_____

Lisa's musing

Oh, that's if you didn't take my advice and give it to someone else to send to you as a surprise. If you did that, instead reach into your gratitude jar and pull out 10 gratitudes and read them out loud. Rereading my gratitudes always gives me such an energy boost.

Send yourself a digital letter to be delivered in one, three or five years' time with **futureme.org**.

DECEMBER 30

GRAB A CUPPA, A WINE OR A KOMBUCHA AND SIT IN A COMFY CHAIR WITH YOUR GRATITUDE JAR. READ EVERY PIECE OF PAPER YOU HAVE IN THERE. PUT ANY ASIDE THAT REALLY MEAN SOMETHING TO YOU.

Use the below space to either stick the gratitudes in, or write them out again, so you can keep coming back to them here as a reference.

Lisa's musing

You deserve this. Relax. Relish. Enjoy.

Join a world-wide community gratitude jar online at **thegratitudejar.com**.

THIS HAS BEEN AN AMAZING YEAR WITH CHALLENGES, SUCCESSES, LAUGHTER AND STRESS. LOOKING BACK, WHAT HAVE BEEN THE MOMENTS, PEOPLE AND PLACES YOU HAVE BEEN THE MOST GRATEFUL FOR?

Write them down on this page and the two pages following.

_____

_____

_____

_____

Thank you. Yes, YOU. Thank you for going on this extraordinary journey with me. When I wrote this (along with the help of my beautiful editor – thank you, Lucy), it was such an amazing exercise. And one bigger than we expected, as it evolved over time. This journal consisted of 365 x 4 pieces of information, exercises, musings and resources for you. So it has been a labour of love, but one that we are both grateful for. It is a joy and a pleasure to connect with and serve so many of you on a daily basis. You are why I do what I do. You inspire me every day. Okay, let's go. Time to turn the page and begin a new year. A new chapter. Big, big love, xx Lisa

Need a new diary for next year? Check out **shop.collectivehub.com** and find a beautiful one!

Lisa Messenger is the vibrant, game-changing founder and CEO of *Collective Hub*. She launched the *Collective Hub* print magazine in 2013 with no experience, in an industry that people said was either dead or dying. Over the next seven years, Collective Hub grew into an international multimedia business and lifestyle platform with multiple verticals across print, digital, events and a co-working space – all of which served to ignite human potential.

For more than 19 years in her own businesses, Lisa has inspired game-changers, thought-leaders, style-makers, entrepreneurs and intrapreneurs across the world. An international speaker and best-selling author, she is an authority on disruption in both the corporate sector and the start-up scene.

Lisa's experience in publishing has seen her produce more than 400 custom-published books for companies and individuals, as well as having authored and co-authored 28 (and counting) herself.

Most notably, Lisa charted her ride to success post-launch of *Collective Hub*, documenting the journey and all its lessons in real time with her best-selling book *Daring & Disruptive: Unleashing the Entrepreneur*, and its sequels, which include *Life & Love: Creating the Dream*; *Money & Mindfulness: Living in Abundance*; *Break-ups & Breakthroughs: Turning an Ending Into a New Beginning*; *Purpose: Find Your Why and the How Will Look After Itself*; *Risk & Resilience, Breaking and Remaking a Brand*; *Work From Wherever: How to Set Yourself Free and Still Achieve*; and *Daily Mantras To Ignite Your Potential*.

Her passion is to challenge individuals and corporations to get out of their comfort zones, find their purpose, change the way they think, and to prove that there is more than one way to do anything. She encourages creativity, innovation, and an entrepreneurial spirit, and lives life to the absolute max.

Most mornings she wakes up and pinches herself at how incredible her life is, but she is also acutely aware and honest about life's bumps and tumbles along the way.

With fans including Sir Richard Branson and *New York Times* best-selling author Bradley Trevor Greive, and a social media following of more than 800,000 across her *Collective Hub* and personal platforms, Lisa's vision is to build a community of like-minded people who want to change the world.

In between being a serial entrepreneur, investor and avid traveller, she loves nothing more than being at home with her dog, Benny, doing some gardening, and collecting as many indoor plants as humanly possible.

Collect all of Lisa Messenger's long-format books!
Buy your copy at: **shop.collectivehub.com**

Love this Journal? And all the questions it asks?
Find the others in the series **shop.collectivehub.com**

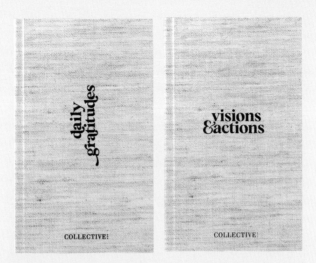

Keep accountable with your gratitudes and goals!
Collective Hub's latest daily check-in journals are a must-have for everyone!

Find more planners and journals like *The Ultimate Writer's Journal* and *The Ultimate Travel Journal* too. Shop them all at **shop.collectivehub.com**

brought to you by
LISA MESSENGER

Learn online!
Dive deep into learning about work/life balance
and location freedom with Lisa Messenger's
The Now of Work digital masterclass!

Available from
shop.collectivehub.com

BOOK LISA FOR AN EVENT!

Lisa is a vibrant, passionate and sought-after global public speaker known for her on-stage wit and insight, and high level of audience engagement.

She is best in Q&A format as she loves to bounce off those around her and drill down to their exact interests, but will happily give keynotes on business, creativity, innovation, start-up growth and challenges, finding your 'why', failing fast, facing your fears, challenging yourself and living your best life.

She's a regular speaker to the corporate and creative communities of Australia, South-East Asia and the United States.

For more info email:
teagan@collectivehub.com

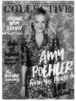